Study Notes for Technicians
Mathematics Level 2

Study Notes for Technicians

Mathematics Level 2

John B. Pratley
BA, MEd, C Eng, MIEE, MIElecIE
The Polytechnic   Wolverhampton

McGRAW-HILL Book Company (UK) Limited

London · New York · St Louis · San Francisco · Auckland
Bogotá · Guatemala · Hamburg · Johannesburg · Lisbon · Madrid
Mexico · Montreal · New Delhi · Panama · Paris · San Juan
São Paulo · Singapore · Sydney · Tokyo · Toronto

Published by
McGRAW-HILL Book Company (UK) Limited
MAIDENHEAD · BERKSHIRE · ENGLAND

British Library Cataloguing in Publication Data
Pratley, John B.
  Study notes for technicians.
  Mathematics level 2.
  1. Mechanical engineering
  I. Title
  621   TJ145
  ISBN 0-07-084865-3

Library of Congress Cataloging in Publication Data
Pratley, John B.
  Study notes for technicians.

  1. Mathematics—1961—   . I. Title.
QA37.2.P68   1984   510   84-23429
ISBN 0-07-084865-3

12345 W.C.L. 8765

Typeset by Oxprint Ltd, Oxford

Printed and bound in Great Britain by
William Clowes Limited, Beccles

Contents

Preface

This book has been written to cover the standard units in:

(a) Mathematics (1) Level 2, TEC U80/691,
(b) Mensuration (2) Level 2, TEC U80/712,
(c) Analytical Mathematics U80/692 Level 2.

The book can also be used in part for
(a) Mathematics at Ordinary level in the General Certificate of Education,
(b) Mathematics in the Certificate of Secondary Education,
(c) YTS and TVEI schemes.

The aim of both TEC units is to
(a) Extend the fundamentals in Mathematics gained in the Level I unit or its equivalent,
(b) Develop the ability to understand and apply mathematical concepts relating to science and technology.

To achieve these aims, the fundamental facts of each topic are summarized, and are followed by numerous worked examples and graded exercises. There are over 130 worked examples and over 700 graded problems for the student to solve. Examples, all to the appropriate level, have been taken, by permission, from tests and examination papers set by the following bodies:

City and Guilds of London Institute	CGLI
East Midlands Further Education Council	EMFEC
Northern Council for Further Education	NCFE
North Western Regional Advisory Council for Further Education	NWRAC
Welsh Joint Education Committee	WJEC
West Midlands Advisory Council for Further Education	WMAC
Yorkshire and Humberside Association for Further and Higher Education	YHCFE

It is acknowledged that the organizations listed above accept no responsibility for model solutions, or answers listed, or any modifications that have been carried out on questions. This responsibility rests with the author.

The author would like to record his special thanks to Graham Saxby and Alison Watkins for giving support during the preparation of this book.

John B Pratley

1 Algebra

1.1 Transposition of formulae

Transposition of formulae means change of subject of a given formula, using the same rules as for the solution of simple equations. These rules can be found in Chapter 2 of *Mathematics Level 1* of this series.

Examples

1. If $W = VIt$ find V in terms of the other quantities.
   Formula: $W = VIt$
   Divide both sides by It: $\dfrac{W}{It} = \dfrac{VIt}{It}$

   Then, $V = \dfrac{W}{It}$

2. If $y = ax + b$ transpose the formula to make b the subject.
   Formula: $y = ax + b$
   Subtract ax from both sides:
   $y - ax = ax + b - ax$
   $y - ax = b$
   Rewritten: $b = y - ax$

3. From $v = u + at$ find a formula for t.
   Formula: $v = u + at$
   Subtract u from both sides: $v - u = at$
   Divide both sides by a: $\dfrac{v - u}{a} = t$

   Rewritten: $t = \dfrac{v - u}{a}$

1.2 Exercises

Change the subject in the following formulae for the letter in parentheses.
1. $PV = mRT$ (T)
2. $V = IR$ (R)
3. $P = \mu W$ (W)
4. $F = ma$ (m)
5. $m = ZIt$ (I)
6. $E = Blv$ (v)
7. $P_1 V_1 = P_2 V_2$ (V_2)
8. $Q = U_2 - U_1$ (U_2)
9. $T = t + 273$ (t)
10. $I = Ig + Is$ (Is)
11. $E = 0.707 E_m$ (E_m)
12. $L = L_0(1 + aT)$ (a)
13. $A = A_0(1 + 2aT)$ (T)
14. $V = V_0(1 + 3aT)$ (V_0)
15. $H = U + mrT$ (T)
16. $C_p = C_v + R$ (R)

1.3 Transposition of formulae containing a root or power

To remove a square root, we square both sides of the equation; to remove a power we take roots of both sides of the equation.

Examples

4. The impedance of a circuit is given by $Z = \sqrt{R^2 + X^2}$.
   Find R in terms of the other quantities.
   Formulae: $Z = \sqrt{R^2 + X^2}$
   Square both sides: $Z^2 = R^2 + X^2$
   Subtract X^2 from both sides:
   $Z^2 - X^2 = R^2$
   Rewritten: $R^2 = Z^2 - X^2$
   Take square roots: $R = \sqrt{Z^2 - X^2}$

5. If $T = 2\pi \sqrt{\dfrac{L}{g}}$ find g in terms of the quantities.

Formula: $T = 2\pi \sqrt{\dfrac{L}{g}}$

Divide both sides by 2π: $\dfrac{T}{2\pi} = \sqrt{\dfrac{L}{g}}$

Square both sides: $\left(\dfrac{T}{2\pi}\right)^2 = \dfrac{L}{g}$

Therefore $\dfrac{T^2}{4\pi^2} = \dfrac{L}{g}$

Multiply both sides by g: $\dfrac{gT^2}{4\pi^2} = L$

Multiply both sides by $4\pi^2$: $gT^2 = 4\pi^2 L$

Divide both sides by T^2: $g = \dfrac{4\pi^2 L}{T^2}$

6. If $v^2 = u^2 + 2as$ find a formula for u.
Formula: $v^2 = u^2 + 2as$
Subtract $2as$ from both sides:
$v^2 - 2as = u^2$
Take square root of both sides:
$\sqrt{v^2 - 2as} = u$
Rewritten: $u = \sqrt{v^2 - 2as}$

1.4 Exercises

1. Given that $I = \dfrac{bd^2}{12}$ find an expression for d.

2. The area of a circle is given by $A = \pi R^2$. Find a formula for R.

3. For a tightly stretched string $n = \dfrac{K\sqrt{T}}{L}$. Make T the subject of the formula.

4. The volume of gas in a furnace chimney is given by $V = \sqrt{\dfrac{2gha(T - t)}{1 + at}}$. Make g the subject of the formula.

5. The volume of a sphere is given by $V = \dfrac{4\pi R^3}{3}$. Make R the subject of the formula.

6. Change the subject in the following formulae for the letter in parentheses.
   (a) $P = I^2 R$ (I)
   (b) $E = mc^2$ (c)
   (c) $W = \frac{1}{2}mV^2$ (V)
   (d) $I = mK^2$ (K)
   (e) $W = I^2 Rt$ (I)
   (f) $P = \dfrac{V^2}{R}$ (V)
   (g) $K^2 = \dfrac{D^2}{8}$ (D)
   (h) $W = \frac{1}{2}LI^2$ (I)
   (i) $g = \dfrac{Gm}{R^2}$ (R)
   (j) $V = \dfrac{\pi d^2 h}{12}$ (d)
   (k) $y = \dfrac{Mx^2}{8EI}$ (x)
   (l) $W = \dfrac{V^2 t}{R}$ (V)
   (m) $A = \dfrac{\pi r^2 \theta}{360}$ (r)
   (n) $Z^2 = R^2 + X^2$ (X)
   (o) $F = \frac{1}{2}m(V^2 - U^2)$ (U)
   (p) $K^2 = K_g + h^2$ (h)
   (q) $S = ut + \frac{1}{2}at^2$ (a)
   (r) $A = P\left(1 + \dfrac{r}{100}\right)^2$ (r)

7. The velocity of water V is given by the formulae $V = \sqrt{\dfrac{H}{dkh}}$. Find k in terms of the other quantities.

8. The diameter of a sphere (D) is given by the formula $D = 3\sqrt{\dfrac{6V}{\pi}}$. Transpose the formulae to find V.

9. Find X from the relationship $T = 2\pi \sqrt{\dfrac{X^2}{gh}}$.

10. Change the subject in the following formulae for the letter in parentheses.
    (a) $V = \sqrt{2gh}$ (h)
    (b) $t = 2\pi \sqrt{LC}$ (L)

(c) $R = \sqrt{F^2 + W^2}$ (W)

(d) $I = \dfrac{V}{\sqrt{R^2 + X^2}}$ (R)

(e) $f = \dfrac{1}{2\pi\sqrt{LC}}$ (L)

(f) $t = \dfrac{\sqrt{2(s - v)}}{a}$ (v)

(g) $S = \sqrt{\dfrac{3d(L - d)}{8}}$ (L)

1.5 Transposition of formulae containing two like terms

The formula containing the unknown quantity in two places is dealt with in a similar manner to the previous sections, except that the two like terms are first manipulated until they are both on the same side of the equals sign. Brackets are then brought into use as shown in the following example.

Examples

7. If $xy = my + k$ find y in terms of the other quantities.
Formulae: $xy = my + k$
Subtract my from both sides: $xy - my = k$
Use a bracket: $y(x - m) = k$
Divide both sides by $(x - m)$:

$$y = \dfrac{k}{(x - m)}$$

8. If $Y = \dfrac{x + Y}{B}$ find a formula for Y.

Formula: $Y = \dfrac{x + Y}{B}$

Multiply both sides by B: $BY = x + Y$
Subtract Y from both sides: $BY - Y = x$
Use a bracket: $Y(B - 1) = x$

Divide both sides by $(B - 1)$: $Y = \dfrac{x}{(B - 1)}$

9. Given that $X = \dfrac{CB}{A + B}$ find an expression for B.

Formula: $X = \dfrac{CB}{A + B}$

Multiply both sides by $(A + B)$:
$X(A + B) = CB$
Remove bracket: $XA + XB = CB$
Subtract XB from both sides:
$XA = CB - XB$
Use a bracket: $XA = B(C - X)$

Divide both sides by $(C - X)$:

$$\dfrac{XA}{(C - X)} = B$$

Rewritten: $B = \dfrac{XA}{(C - X)}$

1.6 Exercises

Transpose the given equations to isolate the subject shown.

1. $AB + CB = K$ (B)
2. $XY = LY + AB$ (Y)
3. $EF - ED = H$ (E)
4. $NM = NA - GH$ (N)
5. $A = \dfrac{B + C}{C}$ (C)
6. $AC = \dfrac{BC - DF}{X}$ (C)
7. $Y = \dfrac{EF}{F + D}$ (F)
8. $Y = \dfrac{x}{x + 1}$ (x)
9. $A = \dfrac{d^2x + d^2y}{b}$ (d)
10. $V = \dfrac{W_1U}{W_1 + W_2}$ (W_1)
11. $y = \dfrac{a - b}{\sqrt{cx + dx}}$ (x)
12. $I = \dfrac{nE}{R + nr}$ (n)
13. $\dfrac{A}{B} = \sqrt{\dfrac{x + y}{x - y}}$ (x)
14. $X = \dfrac{Y(A^2 + B^2)}{A^2 - B^2}$ (B)
15. $T = A(t - k) + t$ (t)
16. $Mv + mu = MV + mU$ (M)

1.7 Evaluation of formulae using a calculator

On the market today there are many different makes of scientific calculators. Each calculator is supplied with an instruction booklet which must be worked through before attempting any of the following examples and exercises. The examples will, however, outline the general procedures common to all calculators. Before starting a calculation, depress the AC key to clear any data left in the calculator from previous operations.

Examples

10. The distance (S) travelled by a body is given by the formula $S = ut + \frac{1}{2}gt^2$. Find S when $u = 2$, $t = 4$ and $g = 10$.
Formula: $S = ut + \frac{1}{2}gt^2$
Substitution $S = (2 \times 4) + (\frac{1}{2} \times 10 \times 4^2)$
Key operation:

　4 $\boxed{\text{INV}}$ $\boxed{x^2}$ × 10 × 0.5 $\boxed{=}$
　$\boxed{\text{M+}}$ 2 × 4 $\boxed{=}$ $\boxed{\text{M+}}$ $\boxed{\text{MR}}$
Readout:
　88

11. If $Z = \dfrac{AX + BY}{A + B}$ determine the value of Z when $A = 36.4$, $B = 30.2$, $X = 1.7$, and $Y = 5.31$.
Formula: $Z = \dfrac{AX + BY}{A + B}$
Substitution:
$Z = \dfrac{(36.4 \times 1.7) + (30.2 \times 5.31)}{36.4 + 30.2}$
Key operation:
　$36.4 \times 1.7 = M+ \ 30.2 \times 5.31 = M+$
　$36.4 + 30.2 = \dfrac{1}{x} \times MR =$
Readout:
　3.336966967

12. Determine the value of A when $A = \sqrt{B^2 + C^2 + D^2}$ and $B = 12.46$, $C = 18.59$, $D = 21.34$.
Formula: $A = \sqrt{B^2 + C^2 + D^2}$
Substitution:
$A = \sqrt{12.46^2 + 18.59^2 + 21.34^2}$
Key operation:
　12.46 INV x² M+ 18.59 INV x² M+
　21.34 INV x² M+ MR $\sqrt{}$
Readout:
　30.9230545

13. If $A = \dfrac{e^{0.6} + e^{-0.6}}{4}$ determine the value of A.
Key operation:
　0.6 INV eˣ M+ 0.6 +/− INV eˣ M+
　MR ÷ 4 =
Readout:
　0.592732609

14. If $T = 2\pi \sqrt{\dfrac{k^2 + h^2}{gh}}$ find the value of T when $k = 4.3$, $h = 6.7$, and $g = 9.81$.
Formula: $T = 2\pi \sqrt{\dfrac{k^2 + h^2}{gh}}$
Substitution: $T = 2\pi \sqrt{\dfrac{4.3^2 + 6.7^2}{9.81 \times 6.7}}$
Key operation:
　4.3 INV x² M+ 6.7 INV x² M+ MR ÷
　9.81 ÷ 6.7 = $\sqrt{}$ × 2 × π =
Readout:
　6.16998461

15. From $y = a \sin B$ find a value for y when $a = 16.7$ and $B = 39°41'$.
Formula: $y = a \sin B$
Substitution: $y = 16.7 \sin 39°41'$
Key operation:
　41 ÷ 60 + 39 = sin × 16.7 =
Readout:
　10.66368449

16. If $A = B \cos 59°43' - C \csc 69°37'$ find A when $B = 18.36$ and $C = 9.43$.

Formula:
$A = B \cos 59°43' - C \csc 69°37'$
Substitution: $A = 18.36 \cos 59°43' - 9.43 \csc 69°37'$

Key operation:
$43 \div 60 + 59 = \cos \times 18.36 = M+ 37$

$\div 60 + 69 = \sin \dfrac{1}{x} \times 9.43 = \text{INV } M-$

MR
Readout:
-0.801402799

17. Given that $y = (a + x)^n$ determine the value of y when $a = 5$, $n = 2.4$ for a range of values of x from -2 to $+2$.
Formula: $y = (a + x)^n$
Substitution when $x = -2$:
$y = (5 + (-2))^{2.4}$
Key operation:
$5 - 2 = x^y \ 2.4 =$
Readout:
13.96661016

x	-2	-1	0	1	2
y	13.96661016	27.85761802	47.59134847	73.7162104	106.7174148

1.8 Exercises

Evaluate the following using a calculator.

1. If $y = abc$ find a value for y when $a = 9.346$, $b = 5278$, and $c = 0.002156$.

2. Determine the value of y if $y = \dfrac{ab + cd}{a + c}$ when $a = 16.4$, $b = 22.9$, $c = 27.56$ and $d = 3.456$.

3. The impedance of a circuit is given by $Z = \sqrt{R^2 + X^2}$. Determine a value for Z when $R = 11.76$ and $X = 22.98$.

4. If $Y = \dfrac{e^{0.8} + e^{1.2}}{1.732}$ determine the value of Y.

5. The volume of a cap is given by $V = \pi h \left(\dfrac{c^2}{8} + \dfrac{h^2}{6} \right)$.
Determine a value for V when $h = 6.732$, $c = 12.91$.

6. From the cosine formula $a^2 = b^2 + c^2 - 2bc \cos A$ determine a value for a when $b = 8.6$, $c = 9.4$, and $A = 136°22'$.

7. Given that $y = (a + x)^n$ determine the value of y when $a = 8$, $n = 1.5$ for a range of values of x from -10 to $+10$.

8. If $y = ab^x$ compile a table of values for y if $a = 3$ and $x = 1, 2, 3, 4$, and 5 when $b = 4$.

9. Given that $y = ab^x$ and x is a constant value of 3.5 determine values of y to complete the given table.

a	-10	-8	-6	-4	0	4	6	8	10
b		2	4	6	8	10	12	14	16	18

10. Calculate B when $A = 6.875$ and $C = 197.5$ given that $B = \dfrac{A + C}{2AC}$.

(NCFE)

11. The minimum radius which a vehicle can negotiate is given by the formula $r = \dfrac{2v^2 h}{ag}$. Determine the value of r when $v = 35$, $h = 0.6734$, $a = 1.314$, and $g = 9.81$.

(EMFEC)

12. If $R_1 = R_0 (1 + \alpha[t_2 - t_1])$ determine R_1 when $R_0 = 21.74$, $t_2 = 60.4$, $t_1 = 18$, and $\alpha = 0.0016$.

(EMFEC)

13. Given that $h = 59.12$ and $r = 17.68$, find x when $x = \sqrt[3]{\dfrac{h + 10}{r - 10}}$.

(NWRAC)

14. The voltage V across a component t seconds after a direct current supply is connected is given by $V = 40(1 - e^{t/100})$. Calculate the voltage 25 seconds after connection.

15. The current i flowing in a circuit t seconds after connecting it to a supply is given by $i = 8(1 - e^{1.5t})$. Find the value of current flowing after a time of 54.8 seconds.

16. When applying a flattening test to a boiler tube, a section of tube is compressed between flat plates. The distance H between plates to which a steel tube of outside diameter D and wall thickness t must be flattened without failure is given by $H = \dfrac{1.09t}{0.09 + \dfrac{t}{D}}$.

Find H when $t = 3.2$ mm and $D = 51$ mm.

(CGLI)

17. The cross-sectional area of an extruded section can be found by using the formula $A = t(2D + B - t)$. If $A = 100$ mm^2 when $D = 16$ mm and $B = 20$ mm, find a logical value for t.

(CGLI)

18. The volume V of the frustum of a cone is $V = \dfrac{\pi h}{3} (R^2 + Rr + r^2)$.

Calculate the volume when $h = 6$ mm, $R = 14$ mm, and $r = 7$ mm.

(CGLI)

19. A close approximation to the length L of the perimeter of an ellipse, whose axes have lengths a and b, is given by the formula:

$$L = \sqrt{\frac{a^2 + b^2}{2} - \frac{(a - b)^2}{8.8}}.$$

Find L when $a = 40$ mm, $b = 24$ mm.

(CGLI)

20. If $\dfrac{1}{R - 1} = \dfrac{3}{1 - t} - \dfrac{4}{1 + t}$ obtain the formula for R, and then find its value when $t = 0.6$.

(NWRAC)

21. The current I in a conductor is given by the expression:

$$I = \frac{0.108}{\dfrac{1}{r_1} + \dfrac{1}{r_2} + \dfrac{1}{r_3} + \dfrac{1}{r_4}}.$$

Calculate I when $r_1 = 8$, $r_2 = 10$, $r_3 = 12$, and $r_4 = 14$.

(WMAC)

22. Given that $f = \sqrt{\dfrac{p^2}{4} + q^2}$, find the value of f when $p = 12$ and $q = 8$.

23. Given that $f = \dfrac{2(s - ut)}{t^2}$, express u in terms of f, s, and t. Find the value of u when $s = 80$, $f = 32$, and $t = 2.5$.

(NCFE)

24. If $R = R_0 (1 + kt)$, find the value of R_0 when $R = 100$, $k = 0.0043$, and $t = 50$.

(NWRAC)

1.9 Accuracy of calculator results

The results calculated in Secs 1.7 and 1.8 give up to a 10-number accuracy. This level of accuracy is not always required, so numbers can be truncated or corrected to a number of significant places or decimal places.

(1) Truncation

A truncated number is one that has a number of digits removed from its end. For example 16.786567 truncated to four figures is 16.78.

(2) Significant figures

To express a number to a number of significant figures, there are two rules:

(a) The first digit that is not a zero becomes the first significant figure.

(b) The figures following are then counted until the total is the number of figures required. If the next number after this is 5 or more, 1 is added to the final significant figure.

For example, 16.786567 correct to four significant figures is 16.79.

(3) Decimal places

A number corrected to a number of decimal places follows two rules:

(a) Start at the right-hand side of the decimal point.

(b) The figures following are then counted until the total is the number of figures required. If the next number after this is 5 or more, 1 is added to the final figure.

For example, 16.786567 correct to one decimal place is 16.8.

Example

18. Complete the given table

1.10 Exercises

1. Truncate the following calculated numbers to the value in parentheses.

   (a) 23.678 999 76 (4)
   (b) 1.465 783 926 (7)
   (c) 675.987 6542 (3)
   (d) 4563.987 639 (5)
   (e) 0.987 654 367 8 (4)
   (f) 0.098 723 4578 (5)
   (g) 65 748.009 874 (5)
   (h) 456 734.873 42 (6)

2. Write down the following to the number of significant figures shown.

   (a) 2534.876 543 (4)
   (b) 7685.356 896 (4)
   (c) 23.758 943 26 (3)
   (d) 64.428 756 94 (3)
   (e) 0.876 534 5637 (4)
   (f) 0.098 365 2424 (3)
   (g) 0.005 467 8392 (5)
   (h) 413.898 756 34 (3)

3. State the following to the number of decimal places shown.

   (a) 54.987 647 83 (2)
   (b) 654.987 3523 (4)
   (c) 6753.234 563 (1)
   (d) 65 473.874 52 (2)
   (e) 0.987 563 4264 (2)
   (f) 0.005 674 9326 (3)
   (g) 0.064 538 9253 (4)
   (h) 0.000 000 6785 (1)

Number	Truncate to four figures	Three significant figures	Two decimal places
16.732 146 89	16.73	16.7	16.73
371.698 7567	371.6	372	371.70
4216.137 482	4216	4220	4216.14
0.986 432 148	0.9864	0.986	0.99
0.098 772 346	0.0987	0.0988	0.10

4. Evaluate, using a calculator, giving the answer correct to two decimal places.

(a) $\dfrac{1}{16.18 \times \sqrt{120}}$ (b) $(0.0014422)^{\frac{1}{2}}$

(EMFEC)

5. If $Y = \sqrt{X} + \dfrac{1}{Z}$, determine the value of Y using a calculator when $X = 650.8$ and $Z = 33.24$. State the answer correct to one decimal place.

(NWRAC)

6. If $D = \dfrac{A^3 + B^2}{C}$, find D when $A = 1.74$, $B = 0.625$, and $C = 0.0066$. State the answer correct to three significant figures.

(YHCFE)

7. Find a value for A when $A = \sqrt{\dfrac{(1.878)^2 + (3.142)^2}{14.4}}$

Use a calculator and state the answer correct to three decimal places.

(NWRAC)

8. Calculate the value of $\dfrac{4.7(P + Q)}{P\sqrt{P^2 - Q^2}}$ when $P = 18.35$ and $Q = 14.85$ correct to two decimal places.

(NCFE)

9. In a belt drive the ratio of the tension T_1 on the tight side of the belt to the tension T_2 on the slack side is given by the equation $\dfrac{T_1}{T_2} = e^{\mu a}$.

Find the value of T_1 and T_2 if $\mu = 0.27$, $a = 165$, and $T_1 - T_2 = 160$. State the answers correct to three significant figures.

(WMAC)

10. Use a calculator to evaluate correct to three significant figures the value of A if $\dfrac{1}{A} = \dfrac{1}{b} + \dfrac{1}{c} + \dfrac{1}{d}$, where $b = 27.6$, $c = 9.4$, and $d = 0.063$.

(EMFEC)

11. The resonant frequency of a circuit containing inductance and capacitance is given by $f = \dfrac{10^6}{2\pi\sqrt{LC}}$. Transpose the formula to find C and determine its value when $f = 1500$ and $L = 25$. State the answer correct to three significant figures.

(CGLI)

12. Evaluate $\dfrac{R^2}{2}(\theta - \sin\theta)$ when $\theta = \dfrac{\pi}{3}$ radians and $R = 4.8$. Give the answer correct to one significant figure.

(WMAC)

13. If $h = \dfrac{12dV^2}{5R}$, find the value of (a) h, correct to one decimal place, when $d = 6\frac{2}{3}$, $V = 30$, and $R = 2500$, (b) V, correct to two significant figures, when $h = 12.96$, $d = 6\frac{2}{3}$, and $R = 2500$.

(NWRAC)

14. Given that $\dfrac{1}{R} = \dfrac{1}{r_1} + \dfrac{1}{r_2} + \dfrac{1}{r_3}$, find R when $r_1 = 0.2$, $r_2 = 2.1$, and $r_3 = 4.2$. Give the answer correct to two decimal places.

(NWRAC)

15. If $V = \dfrac{\pi h}{6}(h^2 + 3r_1^2 + 3r_2^2)$, calculate the value of V when $h = 17.5$, $r_1 = 32.8$, and $r_2 = 43.7$. Give the answer correct to five significant figures.

(EMFEC)

16. If $f = \dfrac{1}{2\pi} \sqrt{\dfrac{1}{LC} - \dfrac{R^2}{4L^2}}$, use a calculator to calculate the value of f if $C = 1.8 \times 10^{-5}$, $L = 0.12$, and $R = 65.3$. State your answer correct to one decimal place.

(EMFEC)

17. The following equation can be used to find the expected tool life between regrinds, under certain conditions of machining: $ST^a f^b = c$ where S = cutting speed, T = tool life, f = feed, and a and b are constants for the material. Calculate the tool life in minutes, correct to two significant figures, when $S = 300$, $c = 190$, $f = 0.01$, $a = 0.25$, and $b = 0.3$.

(CGLI)

1.11 Quadratic equations—solution by factorization

An expression such as $(x + 2)(x + 3)$ is known as a binomial. In a binomial, contents of one pair of brackets are multiplied by the contents of the other.

For example: $(x + 2)(x + 3)$
becomes $x(x + 3) + 2(x + 3)$
becomes $x^2 + 3x + 2x + 6$
becomes $x^2 + 5x + 6$

In general terms we have $ax^2 + bx + c$, where the highest power of the variable is 2. This expression can become a quadratic equation by stating that $ax^2 + bx + c = 0$. A quadratic equation can often be solved by the use of factors.

Examples

19. Solve $x^2 + 6x + 8 = 0$
By inspection $x^2 = (x)(x)$
$8 = (1)(8)$ or $(2)(4)$
Therefore $x^2 + 6x + 8 = (x + 2)(x + 4)$
If $x^2 + 6x + 8 = 0$
then $(x + 2)(x + 4) = 0$

Therefore, either $(x + 2) = 0$ or $(x + 4) = 0$
which gives $x = -2$ or $x = -4$.
The roots of the equation are said to be -2 and -4.

20. Solve $x^2 - 2x - 3 = 0$
By inspection $x^2 = (x)(x)$
$3 = (1)(3)$
Hint: Take extra care with the signs in the brackets.
By factorization $(x + 1)(x - 3) = 0$
So $x + 1 = 0$ or $x - 3 = 0$
which gives $x = -1$ or $x = +3$.

21. Solve $x^2 - 10x + 25 = 0$
By inspection $x^2 = (x)(x)$
$25 = (1)(25)$ or $(5)(5)$
By factorization $(x - 5)(x - 5) = 0$
So $x - 5 = 0$ or $x - 5 = 0$
which gives $x = +5$ or $x = +5$.
Hint: Always check back by performing the multiplication.
That is,
$$(x - 5)(x - 5) = x(x - 5) - 5(x - 5)$$
$$= x^2 - 5x - 5x + 25$$
$$= x^2 - 10x + 25.$$

22. Solve $3x^2 + 14x + 8 = 0$
By inspection $3x^2 = (x)(3x)$
$8 = (1)(8)$ or $(2)(4)$
By factorization $(3x + 2)(x + 4) = 0$
So $3x + 2 = 0$ or $x + 4 = 0$
which gives $3x = -2$ or $x = -4$
That is, $x = -\frac{2}{3}$ or $x = -4$.

23. Deduce a quadratic equation for the following pairs of roots: $-3, 2$.
Given $x = -3$ and $x = 2$
Then $x + 3 = 0$ and $x - 2 = 0$
By factorization $(x + 3)(x - 2) = 0$
Then $x(x - 2) + 3(x - 2) = 0$
$x^2 - 2x + 3x - 6 = 0$
$x^2 + x - 6 = 0.$

1.12 Quadratic equations—solution by completing the square

A quadratic equation $ax^2 + bx + c = 0$ can be solved by using the rules:

(1) Rewrite the equation in the form $ax^2 + bx = c$.
(2) Divide both sides of the equation by the value of a.
(3) Add to each side of the equation the square of one-half the value of b.
(4) Take the square root of each side of the equation and solve the resulting equation for x.

Example

24. Solve $2x^2 - 3x - 4 = 0$ using the method of completing the square.

Equation: $2x^2 - 3x - 4 = 0$

Rule (1) $2x^2 - 3x = +4$

Rule (2) $\dfrac{2x^2 - 3x}{2} = \dfrac{+4}{2}$

$x^2 - 1.5x = +2$

Rule (3)

$x^2 - 1.5x + \left(\dfrac{1.5}{2}\right)^2 = +2 + \left(\dfrac{1.5}{2}\right)^2$

$x^2 - 1.5x + \dfrac{9}{16} = +2 + \dfrac{9}{16}$

$(x - \tfrac{3}{4})^2 = \dfrac{41}{16}$

Rule (4)   Take the square root of each side:

$x - \tfrac{3}{4} = \sqrt{\dfrac{41}{16}}$

$x - \tfrac{3}{4} = \pm\dfrac{6.4}{4} = \pm 1.6$

Solve for x:

$x = +\tfrac{3}{4} + 1.6 \text{ or } +\tfrac{3}{4} - 1.6$

$= 0.75 + 1.6 \text{ or } 0.75 - 1.6$

$= 2.35 \text{ or } -0.85$

1.13 Quadratic equations—solution by formula

The general form of a quadratic equation is $ax^2 + bx + c = 0$. By using the method of completing the squares the following formula can be developed:

$$x = \frac{-b \pm \sqrt{b^2 - 4ac}}{2a}$$

Example

25. Solve the equation $5x^2 - 4x - 3 = 0$ using the formula.

Equation: $5x^2 - 4x - 3 = 0$

$a = 5,\ b = -4,\ \text{and } c = -3$

Formula: $x = \dfrac{-b \pm \sqrt{b^2 - 4ac}}{2a}$

Substitution:

$x = \dfrac{4 \pm \sqrt{(-4)^2 - (4 \times 5 \times -3)}}{2 \times 5}$

$= \dfrac{4 \pm \sqrt{16 + 60}}{10}$

$= \dfrac{4 \pm \sqrt{76}}{10}$

$= \dfrac{4 \pm 8.7}{10}$

Therefore $x = \dfrac{4 + 8.7}{10} = \dfrac{12.7}{10} = 1.27$

or $x = \dfrac{4 - 8.7}{10} = -\dfrac{4.7}{10} = -0.47$

1.14 Exercises

Solve by factors:
1. $x^2 + 5x + 6 = 0$
2. $x^2 + 8x + 7 = 0$
3. $x^2 - x - 12 = 0$
4. $6x^2 + 13x + 6 = 0$
5. $2x^2 + 9x - 5 = 0$
6. $x^2 - 15x + 56 = 0$
7. $x^2 + 49x - 660 = 0$
8. $3x^2 - 10x - 8 = 0$
9. $x(x - 2) - 3(x - 2) = 0$

10. $(x - 5)(x - 7) = 3$
11. $3 - x - 2x^2 = 0$
12. $x^2 - x - 6 = 0$
13. $x^2 = x + 20$
14. $x^2 = 12 - x$
15. $x^2 - 3x = 0$
16. $21 + 10x + x^2 = 0$
17. $x^2 - 7x = -10$
18. $2x^2 - 1 = 1$
19. $\dfrac{x^2}{4} - 3x = -8$
20. $4(2.5x + 6) = x^2$

Find the simplest quadratic equations which have the following roots:

21. 5, 6.   25. −3, −4.   29. 3½, −½.
22. 4, 8.   26. −5, −2.   30. −2½, ⅜.
23. 2, −4. 27. −2, 6.   31. −⅞, −¾.
24. 5, −1. 28. −5, 8.   32. −¼, −⅜.

Solve the following quadratic equations by the method of completing the square:

33. $x^2 - 17x + 60 = 0$
34. $x^2 - 4x = 5$
35. $x^2 - 3x - 5 = 0$
36. $x^2 = -9x - 3$
37. $(x - 3)(x + 4) = 15$
38. $4x^2 - 5x = 6$
39. $7x^2 - 2x - 1 = 0$
40. $x^2 - 2.3x = -1.1$
41. $x^2 + 3.4x = 2.3$
42. $(2x - 1)(3x + 1) = 11$

Solve the following quadratic equations using the formula method:

43. $x^2 + 4x - 32 = 0$
44. $x^2 - 3x + 1 = 0$
45. $x^2 - x - 600 = 0$
46. $2x^2 + 7x + 6 = 0$
47. $4x^2 + 9x + 3 = 0$
48. $x - 10 = x^2 - 10x$
49. $4x^2 + 4x + 1 = 0$
50. $2x^2 + 9.6x + 5.74 = 0$
51. $x + \dfrac{1}{x} - 2 = 0$

52. $x + \dfrac{2}{x} = 4.5$

53. A rectangular hole is cut out from a 125 × 100 mm uniform plate. The distance x between the edge of the plate and edge of the hole is the same on all sides. The hole reduces the weight by 60 per cent.
   (a) Show that $4x^2 - 450x + 5000 = 0$.
   (b) Solve this equation for x and hence determine the dimension of the hole.
   (CGLI)

54. A storage area is rectangular in shape, the dimensions being 60 × 20 mm. The length and breadth are each increased by a distance x so that the area is increased by 43 per cent.
   (a) Show that the value of x can be obtained from the equation
   $$x^2 + 80x - 516 = 0.$$
   (b) Solve this equation for x.
   (CGLI)

55. (a) The total surface area of a cylinder is 220 cm². If d is the diameter and the length is 6.5 cm, taking π as $\dfrac{22}{7}$, show that $d^2 + 13d = 140$.
   (b) Solve this equation for d.
   (CGLI)

56. Solve, by completing the square, the equation $3x^2 + 11x - 42 = 0$.
   (NWRAC)

57. The area of a rectangle of length 8 m and breadth 5 m is unchanged if the length is increased by $4x$ m and the breadth reduced by x m. Form an equation in x and solve it.
   (NWRAC)

58. Solve the equation $2(x^2 - 2x - 3) = 0$.
   (NCFE)

59. (a) Solve the quadratic equation $x^2 - 4x - 12 = 0$ by method of factors.
    (b) Using the formula, solve the quadratic equation: $2x^2 + 3x - 7 = 0$.

    (EMFEC)

60. Solve the equation $x^2 + 3x = 0$.

    (EMFEC)

61. The roots of a quadratic equation are: $x = 1.5$ and $x = -4$. Determine the quadratic equation.

    (EMFEC)

Answers

Exercises 1.2

1. $T = \dfrac{PV}{mR}$

2. $R = \dfrac{V}{I}$

3. $W = \dfrac{P}{\mu}$

4. $m = \dfrac{F}{a}$

5. $I = \dfrac{m}{Zt}$

6. $v = \dfrac{E}{B1}$

7. $V_2 = \dfrac{P_1 V_1}{P_2}$

8. $U_2 = Q + U_1$

9. $t = T - 273$

10. $I_s = I - I_g$

11. $E_m = \dfrac{E}{0.707}$

12. $a = \dfrac{L - L_0}{L_0 T}$

13. $T = \dfrac{A - A_0}{2aA_0}$

14. $V_0 = \dfrac{V}{1 + 3aT}$

15. $T = \dfrac{H - U}{mR}$

16. $R = C_p - C_v$

Exercises 1.4

1. $d = \sqrt{\dfrac{12I}{b}}$

2. $R = \sqrt{\dfrac{A}{\pi}}$

3. $T = \sqrt{\dfrac{nL}{K}}$

4. $g = \dfrac{V^2 (1 + at)}{2ha (T - t)}$

5. $R = 3\sqrt{\dfrac{3V}{4\pi}}$

6. (a) $I = \sqrt{\dfrac{P}{R}}$

   (b) $c = \sqrt{\dfrac{E}{m}}$

   (c) $V = \sqrt{\dfrac{2W}{m}}$

   (d) $K = \sqrt{\dfrac{I}{m}}$

   (e) $I = \sqrt{\dfrac{W}{Rt}}$

   (f) $V = \sqrt{PR}$

   (g) $D = K\sqrt{8}$

   (h) $I = \sqrt{\dfrac{2W}{L}}$

(i) $R = \sqrt{\dfrac{Gm}{g}}$

(j) $d = \sqrt{\dfrac{12V}{\pi h}}$

(k) $x = \sqrt{\dfrac{8EIy}{M}}$

(l) $V = \sqrt{\dfrac{RW}{t}}$

(m) $r = \sqrt{\dfrac{360A}{\pi \theta}}$

(n) $X = \sqrt{Z^2 - R^2}$

(o) $U = \sqrt{V^2 - \dfrac{2F}{m}}$

(p) $h = \sqrt{K^2 - K_g}$

(q) $a = \dfrac{2(S - ut)}{t^2}$

(r) $r = 100\left(\sqrt{\dfrac{A}{P}} - 1 \right)$

7. $k = \dfrac{H}{V^2 dh}$

8. $V = \dfrac{\pi D^3}{6}$

9. $X = \dfrac{T}{2\pi} \sqrt{gh}$

10. (a) $h = \dfrac{V^2}{2g}$

(b) $L = \dfrac{t^2}{4\pi^2 C}$

(c) $W = \sqrt{R^2 - F^2}$

(d) $R = \sqrt{\left(\dfrac{V}{I}\right)^2 - X^2}$

(e) $L = \dfrac{1}{4\pi^2 f^2 C}$

(f) $v = S - \dfrac{(at)^2}{2}$

(g) $L = \dfrac{8S^2}{3d} + d$

Exercises 1.6

1. $B = \dfrac{K}{A + C}$

2. $Y = \dfrac{AB}{X - L}$

3. $E = \dfrac{H}{F - D}$

4. $N = \dfrac{GH}{A - M}$

5. $C = \dfrac{B}{A - 1}$

6. $C = \dfrac{DF}{B - AX}$

7. $F = \dfrac{YD}{E - Y}$

8. $x = \dfrac{y}{1 - y}$

9. $d = \sqrt{\dfrac{Ab}{x + y}}$

10. $W_1 = \dfrac{VW_2}{U - V}$

11. $x = \dfrac{(a - b)^2}{y^2(c + d)}$

12. $n = \dfrac{IR}{E - Ir}$

13. $x = \dfrac{y(A^2 + B^2)}{A^2 - B^2}$

14. $B = A \sqrt{\dfrac{X - Y}{X + Y}}$

15. $t = \dfrac{T + AK}{A + 1}$

16. $M = \dfrac{m(U - u)}{v - V}$

Exercises 1.8

1. 106.351 573 3
2. 10.709 903 55
3. 25.814 298 36
4. 3.201 880 976

14

5. 600.358509
6. 279.33922
7.

x	y
−10	−2.828427125
−5	5.196152422
0	22.627417
+5	46.87216658
+10	76.36753237

8.

x	y
1	12
2	48
3	192
4	768
5	3072

9.

b	y
2	−113.137085
4	−1024
6	−3174.538707
8	−5792.618751
10	0
12	23943.87036
14	61602.64721
16	131072
18	247430.8049

10. 0.075258918
11. 127.9896419
12. 23.2148416
13. 2.080083823
14. −11.36101666
15. −4.00033536
16. 22.83543004
17. 50 or 2
18. 2155.13256
19. 32.54088338
20. 1.2

21. 0.284388714
22. 10
23. −8
24. 82.30452675

Exercises 1.10

1. (a) 23.67
   (b) 1.465783
   (c) 675
   (d) 4563.9
   (e) 0.9876
   (f) 0.09872
   (g) 65748
   (h) 456734

2. (a) 2535
   (b) 7685
   (c) 23.8
   (d) 64.4
   (e) 0.8765
   (f) 0.0984
   (g) 0.0054678
   (h) 414

3. (a) 54.99
   (b) 654.9874
   (c) 6753.2
   (d) 65473.87
   (e) 0.99
   (f) 0.006
   (g) 0.0645
   (h) 0

4. (a) 0.01
   (b) 0.04
5. 25.5
6. 857
7. 0.965
8. 0.79
9. $T_1 = 290$
   $T_2 = 130$
10. 0.0624
11. 450
12. 2
13. (a) 5.8
    (b) 45

14.   0.18
15.   84875
16.   99.3
17.   40

Exercises 1.14

1. $-3, -2$
2. $-7, -1$
3. $4, -3$
4. $-\frac{2}{3}, -1\frac{1}{2}$
5. $\frac{1}{2}, -5$
6. $7, 8$
7. $11, -60$
8. $-\frac{2}{3}, 4$
9. $2, 3$
10. $4, 8$
11. $1, -1.5$
12. $3, -2$
13. $5, -4$
14. $-4, 3$
15. $0, 3$
16. $-7, -3$
17. $5, 2$
18. $1, -1$
19. $4, 8$
20. $12, -2$
21. $x^2 - 11x + 30 = 0$
22. $x^2 - 12x + 32 = 0$
23. $x^2 + 2x - 8 = 0$
24. $x^2 - 4x - 5 = 0$
25. $x^2 + 7x + 12 = 0$
26. $x^2 + 7x + 10 = 0$
27. $x^2 - 4x - 12 = 0$

28. $x^2 - 3x - 40 = 0$
29. $4x^2 - 12x - 7 = 0$
30. $16x^2 + 34x - 15 = 0$
31. $32x^2 + 52x + 21 = 0$
32. $32x^2 + 20x + 3 = 0$
33. $5, 12$
34. $5, -1$
35. $4.2, -1.2$
36. $-0.4, -8.7$
37. $4.7, -5.7$
38. $-0.75, 2$
39. $-0.26, 0.55$
40. $1,62, 0.68$
41. $0.58, -3.98$
42. $1.5, -1\frac{1}{3}$
43. $-8, 4$
44. $2.62, 0.38$
45. $25, -24$
46. $-2, -1.5$
47. $-1.84, -0.41$
48. $10, 1$
49. $-\frac{1}{2}, -\frac{1}{2}$
50. $-4.1, -0.7$
51. $1, 1$
52. $4, 0.5$
53. 100×75 mm
54. 6 m
55. 7 cm
56. $2\frac{1}{3}, -6$
57. $0, 3$
58. $3, -1$
59. $6, -2$
      $-2.77, 1.27$
60. $0, -3$
61. $x^2 + 2.5x - 6 = 0$

2 Graphs

2.1 Straight-line graph—intercept and slope

A straight-line graph is always connected by the equation $Y = mX + c$ where c is the intercept of the straight line and m is the slope often called the gradient.

The intercept is the value on the Y axis that is cut by the straight line.

A straight-line graph has a positive slope if the Y value increases as the X value increases and a negative slope if the Y value decreases as the X value increases.

Examples

1. Draw a straight-line graph from the following figures, and from the straight line state the value of the intercept.

X	0	2	4	6	8	10	12	14	16
Y	5	10	15	20	25	30	35	40	45

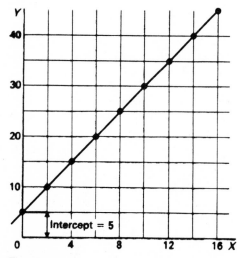

Figure 2.1

2. Write down the intercept values for the graphs drawn in Figs. 2.2 and 2.3

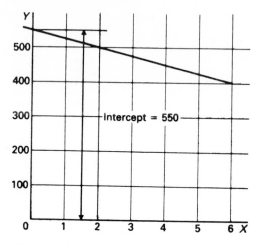

Figure 2.2

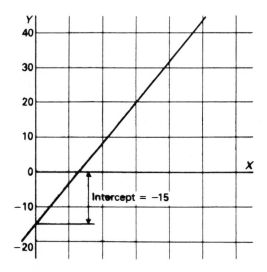

Figure 2.3

3. State in the table provided which graphs have positive and which have negative slopes.

16

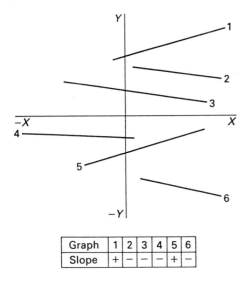

Graph	1	2	3	4	5	6
Slope	+	−	−	−	+	−

Figure 2.4

2.2 Straight-line graph law

To state the straight-line graph law the value of the intercept (c) and slope (m) must be found from the graph and placed in the equation $Y = mX + c$.

The slope of a straight-line graph can be calculated as follows:
(a) Choose any two points on the straight line;
(b) Read the coordinates of each point;
(c) Calculate the difference between the two vertical points;
(d) Calculate the difference between the two horizontal points;
(e) Calculate the slope of the straight-line graph using the formula:

$$\text{Slope} = \frac{\text{difference between the two vertical points}}{\text{difference between the two horizontal points}}$$

Examples

4. A test on a resistor gave the following results:

Resistance (R)	3.2	3.4	3.6	3.8	4.0	4.2	4.4	4.6
Temperature (T)	20	30	40	50	60	70	80	90

Draw a straight-line graph and from it determine the intercept and slope to give a law in the form $R = mT + c$.

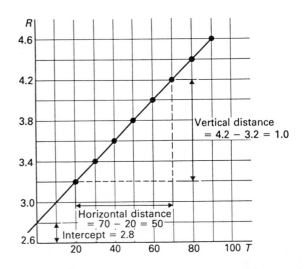

Figure 2.5

From the graph:
Intercept (c) $= 2.8$

$$\text{Slope}\,(m) = \frac{\text{vertical distance}}{\text{horizontal distance}}$$

$$= \frac{1.0}{50} = 0.02$$

Straight-line law: $R = mT + c$
$$R = 0.02T + 2.8$$

Points to note:
(a) The intercept is always measured from the zero of the vertical axis.
(b) The slope of a straight line is always the same wherever the two points are chosen.
(c) Choose two points that are as far apart as is reasonably possible.
(d) Try to choose points that make the horizontal distance a whole number; this makes the division calculation easier.

18

(e) With experimental data the points will not lie on an exact straight line, so a best straight line is drawn with points being evenly distributed on either side of it.

2.3 Exercises

1. Find the intercept and slope for each of the graphs drawn in Fig. 2.6. State for each graph whether the slope is positive or negative.

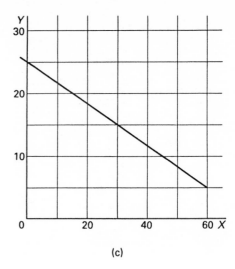

(c)

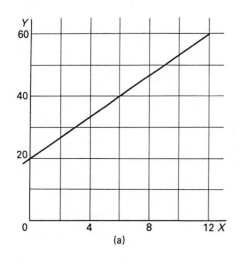

(a)

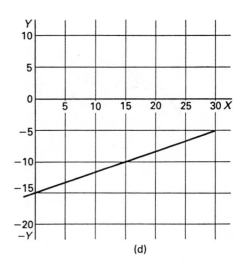

(d)

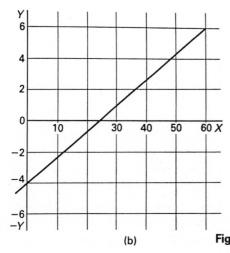

(b)

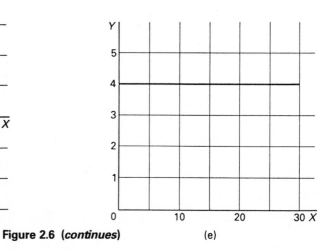

(e)

Figure 2.6 (*continues*)

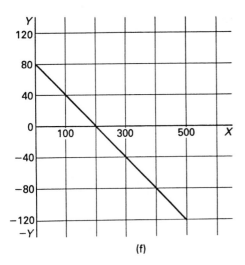

(f)

Figure 2.6

2. In a test on a metal bar the following results were obtained:

Load (N)	10	20	30	40	50	60
Extension (mm)	0.1	0.15	0.2	0.25	0.3	0.35

The load (L) and the extension (E) are thought to be related by a law in the form $E = mL + c$. Show graphically that this is so and find the straight-line law.

3. In an experiment on a crane the load lifted (W) and the corresponding effort (E) required were found to be as follows:

W (N)	14.0	42.0	84.0	112.0
E (N)	5.1	13.3	26.0	35.3

Plot as large a scale as your paper will allow E vertically against W horizontally, draw a straight line to lie evenly among the points obtained and write down the scales used. Using the graph and assuming that E and W are connected by a law

of the form $E = aW + b$, where a and b are numbers, find the values of a and b.
(WMAC)

4. In a test on a steel bar the following values of load (W) and extension (E) were found. Some of the values are missing.

W	2.00		6.50	8.50	10.00	12.00
E	0.64	0.84	1.54	1.94		2.64

W and E are thought to be related by a law of the form $E = aW + b$. Show graphically that this is so and find the values of a and b. Insert the missing values in the table.
(EMFEC)

5. By experiment, the following relationship is found between two quantities R and D.

R	10.5	15.8	21.3	26.6	31.6	36.4	42.0
D	0	1.0	2.0	3.0	4.0	5.0	6.0

It is believed that this relationship can be expressed by an equation of the form $R = mD + c$.

Plot the results and from your graph determine the values of m and c.
(NWRAC)

6. The table below gives the resistance, R ohms, of a length of wire at various temperatures, t degrees Celcius.

Resistance R	23.8	27.2	33.4	37.2	40.3
Temperature t (°C)	50.0	95.0	160.0	205.0	250.0

Show that the law $R = at + b$ is approximately true and estimate values for the constants a and b. At what temperature is the resistance 30 ohms?

(CGLI)

Before attempting the next series of exercises read the following:

The standard straight-line law is $Y = mX + c$ where X and Y are variable quantities and m and c are contants. Other types of equations can be used but are treated in a similar manner to $Y = mX + c$. Consider the following:

(a) $Y = mX^2 + c$. Plot Y against X^2

(b) $Y = m\sqrt{X} + c$. Plot Y against $\sqrt{X}$

(c) $Y = \dfrac{m}{X} + c$. Plot Y against $\dfrac{1}{X}$

7. The following table gives related values of x and y. Determine whether these values are connected by an equation of the form $y = ax^2 + b$, where a and b are constants, and if so, find the values of a and b.

x	4	5	6	7	8	9
y	14.3	18	22.5	28	34.5	41.5

(NWRAC)

8. The following values of R and V satisfy a law of the form $R = a + bV^2$, where a and b are constants.

V	20	25	30	35	40	45
R	52	58	67	76	88	100

Plot suitable quantities to obtain a straight-line graph and obtain the values of a and b.

(NWRAC)

9. The following values of capacitance and reactance in a series L-C circuit were obtained by measurement:

X (Ω)	0	9	21	25	34	38	40
C (μF)		0.2	0.25	0.4	0.5	1.0	2.0	4.0

The law connecting the two variables is $X = a + \dfrac{b}{C}$. By suitable plotting, obtain values for a and b from a straight-line graph.

(EMFEC)

10. Two quantities y and x are believed to be connected by a law of the form $y = m\sqrt{x} + c$. The following values were obtained from an investigation:

x	4	9	16	25	36	49	64
y	5.4	6.8	8.2	9.6	11.0	12.4	13.8

Draw a suitable graph to test if y and x are connected by the law, and determine the probable values of m and c. Using the law find the value of y when $x = 160$.

11. A test performed on an electronic component to show the relationship between current and applied voltage obtained the following results:

Applied voltage V (V)	4	7	11	14	17	20
Current i (mA)	1.17	1.46	1.77	1.97	2.15	2.32

The law connecting V and i is in the form $V = ai^2 + b$. Verify this by producing a suitable straight-line graph and find the values of a and b.

(EMFEC)

12. Two variables are related by the law $y = a\sqrt{x} + b$.

x	1	3	6	10	18
y	1.80	2.24	2.67	3.10	3.75

Plot a graph from the values of x and y to verify the relationship and from it determine the values of constants a and b.

(EMFEC)

13. The relationship between x and y in the table is $y = \dfrac{b}{x} + a$.

x	60.1	49.5	42.4	36.8	32.7
y	4	5	6	7	8

Produce a straight-line graph by plotting suitable variables, and from this obtain the values of a and b.

(EMFEC)

14. The observed quantities of two variables x and y are given in the table:

x	1	2	3	4	5
y	2.2	3.7	6.2	9.7	14.2

The values are related by the law $y = ax^2 + b$. Plot a suitable graph to verify this law and determine the probable values of a and b.

(EMFEC)

15. Two variables, x and y, are related by the law $y = \dfrac{a}{x} + b$.

x	1	2	3	4	5	6
y	2.1	0.9	0.5	0.3	0.2	0.1

Plot a suitable graph to verify the law and determine the values of a and b. From the graph find the value of y when $x = 2.5$

(EMFEC)

16. Two quantities W and H are believed to be connected by a law of the form

$$W = \frac{m}{\sqrt{H}} + c.$$

W	5.02	4.50	4.13	4.04	3.97	3.92
H	4	6	8	10	12	14

Draw a suitable graph to test if W and H are connected by the law, and determine the probable values of m and c. Using the law find the value of H when $W = 4.25$.

(WMAC)

17. Variables x and y are related by the law $y = \dfrac{a}{x} + b$, where a and b are constants. Corresponding values of x and y are tabulated:

x	1	2	3	4	5
y	8.0	2.0	0	−1.0	−1.6

By plotting a suitable graph, verify this relationship and obtain the values of a and b.

(EMFEC)

2.4 Graphical solution of simultaneous equations

Two equations containing two unknowns such as $y - 4x = 2$ and $2y - 6x = 8$, such that only one value of x and one value of y exist that will satisfy both equations, are called simultaneous equations. Simultaneous equations can either be solved by elimination or

22

substitution. Full details of these methods can be found in Chapter 2 of Mathematics Level 1 of this series. To solve simultaneous equations graphically, a graph of each equation is plotted on the same axes and the same scale, the solution being given by the co-ordinates of the point where the two graphs cross.

Examples

5. Solve, graphically, the simultaneous equation for x and y:

$$y - 4x = 2$$
$$2y - 6x = 8$$

Each equation is rearranged to the form of the straight-line law:

$$y = 4x + 2 \qquad \text{Equation 1}$$
$$y = 3x + 4 \qquad \text{Equation 2}$$

A table of values is drawn up for y assuming a range of values for x from 0 to 5.

Equation 1. $y = 4x + 2$
Let $x = 0$ then $y = (4 \times 0) + 2 = 2$

x	0	1	2	3	4	5
y	2	6	10	14	18	22

Equation 2. $y = 3x + 4$
Let $x = 0$ then $y = (3 \times 0) + 4 = 4$

x	0	1	2	3	4	5
y	4	7	10	13	16	19

The intersection is at $(2, 10)$; therefore $x = 2$ and $y = 10$.

6. Solve the simultaneous equation $2y - 3x = 6$ and $y - 2x = 5$ by plotting graphs over the range from $x = -5$ to $x = +5$.
Equation 1
From $2y - 3x = 6$, $y = 1.5x + 3$
Equation 2
From $y - 2x = 5$, $y = 2x + 5$

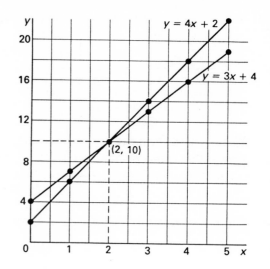

Figure 2.7

Equation 1. $y = 1.5x + 3$

x	−5	−4	−3	−2	1	0	1	2	3	4	5
y	4.5	−3	1.5	0	15	3	45	6	75	9	10.5

Equation 2. $y = 2x + 5$

x	−5	−4	−3	−2	−1	0	1	2	3	4	5
y	−5	−3	−1	−1	3	5	7	9	11	13	15

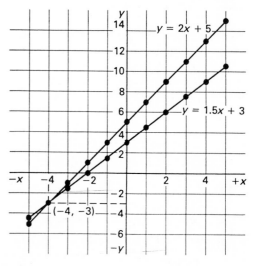

Figure 2.8

The intersection is at $(-4, -3)$; therefore $x = -4$ and $y = -3$.

2.5 The graph of $y = ax^2$

Whenever a graph of the type $y = ax^2$ is plotted, its shape will always follow the form of a parabola. The value of a can either be positive or negative.

Example

7. Plot the graph of $y = x^2$ for values of x from -6 to $+6$.

x	-6	-5	-4	-3	-2	-1	0	1	2	3	4	5	6
y	36	25	16	9	4	1	0	1	4	9	16	25	36

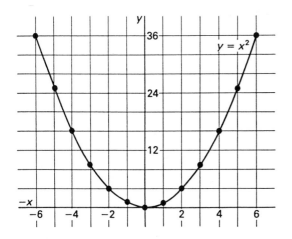

Figure 2.9

8. Plot the graph of $y = -x^2$ for values of x from -6 to $+6$

x	-6	-5	-4	-3	-2	-1	0	1	2	3	4	5	6
y	-36	-25	-16	-9	-4	-1	0	-1	-4	-9	-16	-25	-36

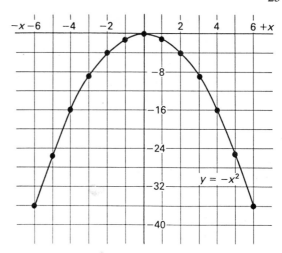

Figure 2.10

9. Plot the graph of $y = 3x^2$ for values of x from -10 to $+10$.

x	-10	-8	-6	-4	-2	0	2	4	6	8	10
y	300	192	108	48	12	0	12	48	108	192	300

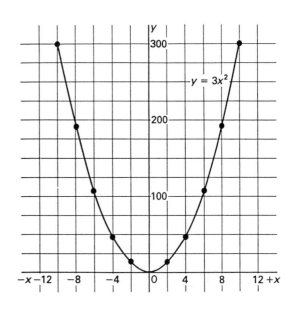

Figure 2.11

2.6 Graphical solution of quadratic equations of the type $y = ax^2 + bx + c$

The values of a, b, and c in the equation $y = ax^2 + bx + c$ can be positive or negative.

The quadratic equation can be solved by using one of two graphical methods:

(a) When a graph of $y = ax^2 + bx + c$ is plotted and it cuts the x axis, the points of intersection give the values of x that satisfy the equation.

(b) The equation $ax^2 + bx + c$ is rearranged to read $ax^2 = -bx - c$. Two graphs are drawn; one of $y = ax^2$ and the other of $y = -bx - c$. The values of x at the points of intersection gives the solution of the equation $y = ax^2 + bx + c$.

In this example a range of values was given for x; this is not always the case. To compile a successful table it is recommended that values of y are worked out from $x = 0$ and working in both negative and positive directions until a change of sign occurs indicating that the graph will cross the x axis.

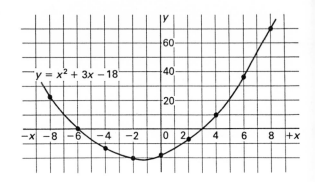

Figure 2.12

Examples

10. Solve the quadratic equation $x^2 + 3x - 18 = 0$ for values of x from -8 to $+8$ by plotting a graph of the form $y = ax^2 + bx + c$.

    A table is compiled by taking values of x; a specimen calculation is given for $x = 2$

    $$y = x^2 + 3x - 18$$
    $$= 2^2 + (3 \times 2) - 18$$
    $$= 4 + 6 - 18$$
    $$= -8$$

x	-8	-6	-4	-2	0	2	4	6	8
x^2	64	36	16	4	0	4	16	36	64
$+3x$	-24	-18	-12	-6	0	6	12	18	24$-$
-18	-18	-18	-18	-18	-18	-18	-18	-18	-18
y	22	0	-14	-20	-18	-8	10	36	70

From the graph $x = -6$, or $+3$.

11. Solve the equation $x^2 - x - 72 = 0$ by plotting $y = x^2$ and $y = x + 72$ between $x = -10$ on the same axes.

    Consider the equation $y = x^2$

x	-10	-8	-6	-4	-2	0	2	4	6	8	10
y	100	64	36	16	4	0	4	16	36	64	100

Consider the equation $y = x + 72$

x	-10	-8	-6	-4	-2	0	2	4	6	8	10
y	62	64	66	68	70	72	76	78	78	80	82

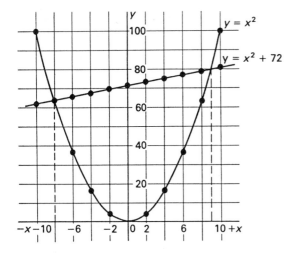

Figure 2.13

From the graph $x = 9$, or -8.

2.7 Exercises

1. Solve graphically the following equations:
   (a) $4x + 10y = 46$ (d) $4x - 10y = 2$
   $6x + 8y = 48$ $14x + 6y = 48$
   (b) $6x + 14y = 54$ (e) $16x - 2y = 68$
   $10x + 4y = 32$ $2x + 16y = 106$
   (c) $14x + 4y = 94$ (f) $10x - 14y = -42$
   $10x - 8y = 2$ $42x - 18y = 150$

2. Solve the simultaneous equations $2x - y = 9$ and $3x - 7y = 19$ by plotting graphs over the range of $x = -5$ to $x = +5$.

3. By drawing graphs within the range $x = -5$ to $x = 20$, solve the simultaneous equations:
   $$19x + 17y = 0$$
   $$2x - y = 53$$

4. Solve the following simultaneous equations graphically by noting the point of intersection of the pairs of straight lines.
   $$3x + 4y = 18$$
   $$4x - 2y = 2$$

5. Plot the graph of $y = x^2$ for values of x from -10 to $+10$.

6. Plot the graphs of $y = x^2$, $y = 0.5x^2$, $y = 2x^2$, and $y = 3x^2$ for values of x from -5 to $+5$, all on the same axes.

7. Plot the graph of $y = -x^2$ for values of x from -10 to $+10$.

8. Plot the graphs of $y = -0.5x^2$, $y = -x^2$, $y = -1.5x^2$, $y = -2x^2$, and $y = -3x^2$ for values of x from -5 to $+5$, all on the same axes.

9. Solve the following quadratic equations using the one-graph method:
   (a) $x^2 + 2x - 120 = 0$
   (b) $x^2 + x - 72 = 0$
   (c) $x^2 - 3x + 2 = 0$
   (d) $x^2 - 11x + 16 = 0$
   (e) $x^2 + 3x + 2 = 0$
   (f) $3x^2 + 15x + 12 = 0$
   (g) $x^2 + 11x + 30 = 0$
   (h) $10x^2 - 30x + 20 = 0$
   (i) $16x^2 - 64x + 48 = 0$
   (j) $3x^2 - 2x - 1 = 0$

10. Solve the following quadratic equations using the two-graph method:
    (a) $x^2 + 3x - 18 = 0$
    (b) $x^2 + 5x - 14 = 0$
    (c) $x^2 - 5x - 36 = 0$
    (d) $x^2 - x - 72 = 0$
    (e) $x^2 - 13x + 42 = 0$
    (f) $x^2 - 10x + 21 = 0$
    (g) $x^2 - 7x + 12 = 0$

11. Draw the graph of $y = 4x^2 - 8x - 7$ from $x = -3$ to $x = 5$. Find the values of x which make $y = 0$.
    (EMFEC)

12. Graph each of the functions $\frac{1}{2}x^2$ and $(3 - 0.4x)$ for values of x from -3.5 to $+3.5$ using the same scales and reference axes for both graphs. By means of the graphs estimate the values of x for which $\frac{1}{2}x^2 = 3 - 0.4x$.
    (NCFE)

2.8 The graph of $y = ax^3$

The value of a in the equation can either be positive or negative; the effect being shown in the following examples.

Examples

12. Plot the graph of $y = x^3$ with values of x ranging from $x = -5$ to $x = +5$.
    To draw the graph we compile the following table

x	-5	-4	-3	-2	-1	0	1	2	3	4	5
y	-125	-64	-27	-8	-1	0	1	8	27	64	125

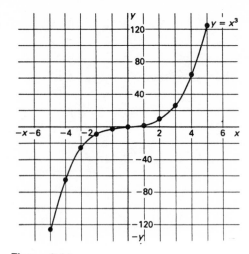

Figure 2.14

13. Plot the graph of $y = 4x^3$ with values of x ranging from $x = -5$ to $x = +5$.

x	-5	-4	-3	-2	-1	0	1	2	3	4	5
y	-500	-256	-108	-32	-4	0	4	32	108	256	500

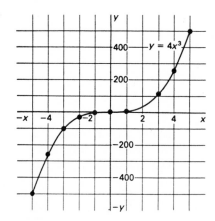

Figure 2.15

14. Plot the graph of $y = -x^3$ with values of x ranging from $x = -5$ to $x = +5$.

x	-5	-4	-3	-2	-1	0	1	2	3	4	5
y	125	64	27	8	1	0	-1	-8	-27	-64	-125

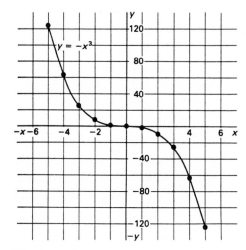

Figure 2.16

2.9 Graphical solution of equations of the type $y = ax^3 + bx^2 + cx + d$

An S-shaped curve is characteristic of functions of the type $y = ax^3 + bx^2 + cx + d$ where a, b, c, or d can be positive or negative values. Such a curve will cross the x axis either three times or only once. These values give the roots of the equation.

Examples

15. Solve the following equation: $x^3 + 2x^2 - 20x - 100 = 0$

    To compile the table we assume values ranging from $x = -10$ to $x = +10$.

x	-10	-8	-6	-4	-2	0	2	4	6	8	10
x^3	-1000	-512	-216	-64	-8	0	8	64	216	512	1000
$2x^2$	200	128	72	32	8	0	8	32	72	128	200
$-20x$	200	160	120	80	40	0	-40	-80	-120	-160	-200
-100	-100	-100	-100	-100	-100	-100	-100	-100	-100	-100	-100
y	-700	-324	-124	-52	-60	-100	-124	-84	68	380	900

Inspection of the graph shows that the value of x is 5.3. If a more accurate value was needed we could now plot a graph with values of x ranging from $x = +5$ to $x = +6$.

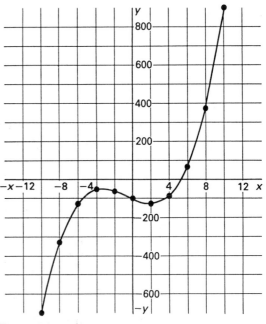

Figure 2.17

16. Solve the equation $x^3 - 9x^2 + 26x - 24 = 0$ graphically using a range of values of $x = 0.5$ to $x = 4.5$.

x	0.5	1	1.5	2	2.5	3	3.5	4	4.5
x^3	0.125	1	3.375	8	15.625	27	42.875	64	91.125
$-9x^2$	−2.25	−9	−20.25	−36	−56.25	81	−110.25	−144	−182.25
$26x$	13	26	39	52	65	78	91	104	117
-24	−24	−24	−24	−24	−24	−24	−24	−24	−24
y	−13.125	−6	−1.875	0	0.4	0	−0.375	0	−1.875

Inspection of the graph shows that $x = 2$, 3, and 4.

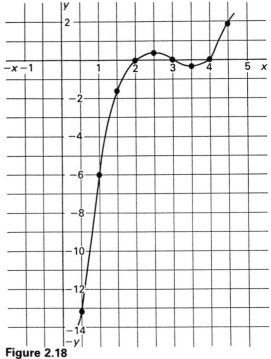

Figure 2.18

17. Solve the equation $x^3 - 3x - 1 = 0$ given a range of values of x from $x = -2$ to $x = +2$.

x	−2	−1.5	−1	−0.5	0	0.5	1	1.5	2
x^2	−8	−3.375	−1	−0.125	0	0.125	1	3.375	8
$-3x$	6	4.5	3	1.5	0	−1.5	−3	−4.5	−6
-1	−1	−1	−1	−1	−1	−1	−1	−1	−1
y	−3	0.125	1	0.375	−1	−2.375	−3	−2.125	1

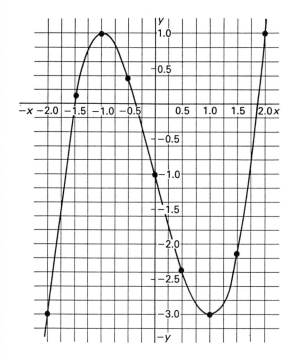

Figure 2.19

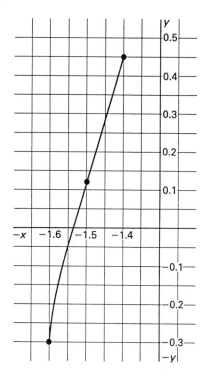

Figure 2.20

From the graph $x = -1.5$, -0.38, and $+1.9$.

It is fairly obvious that these values are approximate, and to obtain a more accurate result further graphs need to be drawn using values around the initial findings as shown in Fig. 2.20 for $x = -1.5$, Fig. 2.21 for $x = -0.38$, and Fig. 2.22 for $x = 1.9$.

Figure 2.20
From the graph $x = -1.53$

Figure 2.21
From the graph $x = -0.35$

Figure 2.22
From the graph $x = 1.88$
For the equation $x^3 - 3x - 1 = 0$ the values of x are $x = -1.53$, -0.35, and 1.88.

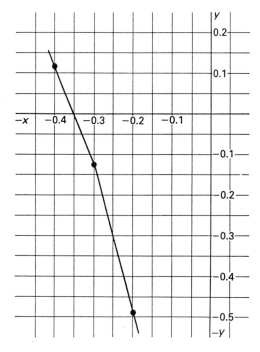

Figure 2.21

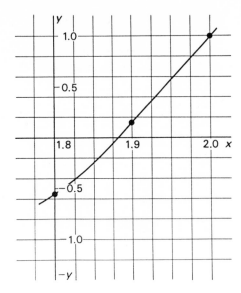

Figure 2.22

2.10 Exercises

1. Show graphically that the following equations have only one root, and find the value of that root.
   (a) $x^3 - 2x - 3 = 0$
   (b) $x^3 + 3x - 4 = 0$
   (c) $2x^3 - x - 2 = 0$
   (d) $x^3 - x^2 - x - 2 = 0$
   (e) $x^3 + 2x^2 - 20x - 100 = 0$

2. Use a graphical method to find the roots of the following equations:
   (a) $x^3 - 3x + 2 = 0$. Use a range of $x = -2.5$ to $x = +2.5$.
   (b) $x^3 - 3.75x + 1.5 = 0$. Use a range of $x = -3$ to $x = +3$.
   (c) $10x^3 - 50x + 18 = 0$. Use a range of $x = -3$ to $x = +3$.
   (d) $x^3 - 2x^2 + 1 = 0$. Use a range of $x = -0.8$ to $x = +1.8$.
   (e) $x^3 - 3x^2 - 2x + 1 = 0$. Use a range of $x = -1$ to $x = +4$.

3. Solve the following equations graphically:
   (a) $x^3 - 2x^2 - x + 2 = 0$
   (b) $x^3 - 3x^2 + 2x + 4 = 0$

   (c) $x^3 + 2x^2 - x - 1 = 0$
   (d) $x^3 + 4.8x + 2 = 0$
   (e) $0.2x^3 - 11.2x + 6.4 = 0$

4. Plot the curve of the equation $y = 2x^3 - 5x^2 + 2$ between the values $x = -2$ and $x = 3$, and from your curve find the roots of the equation $2x^3 - 5x^2 + 2 = 0$.
   (NWRAC)

5. Find to two significant figures the values of x between $+3$ and -3 which satisfy the equation $x^3 - 6x + 3 = 0$.
   (NWRAC)

6. Graph the function $0.1(x - 1)(2x + 3)(2x - 7)$ for all values of x from -2 to $+4$. By means of the graph, estimate the roots of the equation
   $0.1(x - 1)(2x + 3)(2x - 7) = 5$
   (NCFE)

7. Graph the function $\dfrac{1}{5}(x - 4)^2(x + 2)$ for values of x from -2 to $+6$. By means of the graph solve each of the equations
   (a) $(x - 4)^2(x + 2) = 10$
   (b) $(x - 4)^2(x + 2) = 17$
   (NCFE)

8. Draw the graph of $y = x^3 - 2x^2 - 3x + 4$ for values of x from -2 to $+3$ at unit intervals. Use your graph to solve the following equation
   $x^3 - 2x^2 - 3x + 4 = 0$
   (EMFEC)

9. Draw the graph of $y = 4x^3 - 4x^2 - 10x + 3$ for values of x from -2 to $+3$ at unit intervals and hence solve the cubic equation $4x^3 - 4x^2 - 10x + 3 = 0$.
   (EMFEC)

10. Draw the graph of $y = x^3 - 1.5x^2 - 6x + 5$ for values of x from -3 to $+4$ at unit intervals. Use the graph to solve the equation:
    $x^3 - 1.5x^2 - 6x + 5 = 0$
    (EMFEC)

2.11 The graph of $y = ax^n$

A graph of this type needs a calculation that can be carried out either by using logarithms or by using a calculator.

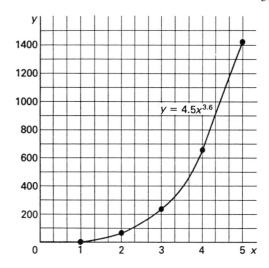

Figure 2.23

Examples

18. Draw the graph of $y = 4.5x^{3.6}$ for values of x from $x = 0$ to $x = 5$.
    By logarithms:
    Equation: $y = 4.5x^{3.6}$
    Take logs of both sides: $\log y = \log 4.5 + 3.6 \log x$
    Complete a table as shown below.

x	0	1	2	3	4	5
$\log x$	$-\infty$	0	0.3010	0.4771	0.6021	0.6990
$3.6 \log x$	$-\infty$	0	1.0840	1.7176	2.1676	2.5164
$\log 4.5$	0.6532	0.6532	0.6532	0.6532	0.6532	0.6532
$\log y$	$-\infty$	0.6532	1.7372	2.3708	2.8208	3.1496
y	0	4.5	54.55	234.8	661.9	1411

By calculator:
Equation: $y = 4.5x^{3.6}$. Consider $x = 5$
Key operation:
$$5 \; x^y \; 3.6 \; = \; \times \; 4.5 \; =$$
Readout:
$\quad 1477.42189 = 1477$ correct to four significant figures.
The remaining values can be calculated in a like manner.

x	0	1	2.	3	4	5
y	0	4.5	54.57	234.9	661.7	1477

19. The following values of x and y follow a law of the type $y = ax^n$. By plotting a graph $\log y$ (vertically) against $\log x$ find values for a and n.

x	1	2	3	4	5
y	2.5	10	22.5	40	62.5

Equation: $y = ax^n$
Take logs of both sides:
$\log y = n \log x + \log a$
Note: This equation now follows the form of a straight-line graph and can be solved by using the method given in Sec. 2.2, where n is the intercept and $\log a$ is the slope.

$\log y$	0.3979	1.0000	1.3522	1.6021	1.7959
$\log x$	0	0.3010	0.4771	0.6021	0.6990

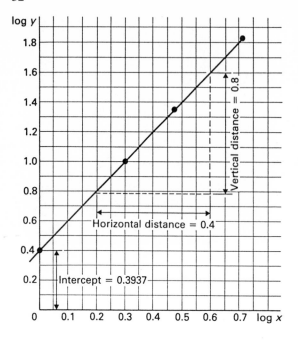

Figure 2.24

x	0	0.5	1.0	1.5	2.0	2.5
$1.34x$	0	0.67	1.34	2.01	2.68	3.35
$1.34x \log e$	0	0.2910	0.5820	0.8729	1.1639	1.455
$\log 3$	0.4771	0.4771	0.4771	0.4771	0.4771	0.477
$\log y$	0.4771	0.7681	1.0591	1.3500	1.6410	1.932
y	3	5.862	11.46	22.39	43.75	85.53

By calculator
Equation: $y = 3e^{1.34x}$. Consider $x = 2.5$
Key operation:
$$1.34 \times 2.5 = \text{INV } e^x \times 3 =$$
Readout:
$85.50820093 = 85.51$ correct to two decimal places

From the graph:
Intercept $= \log a = 0.3979$
By taking the antilog of 0.3979 $a = 2.5$
$$\text{Slope} = \frac{\text{vertical distance}}{\text{horizontal distance}} = \frac{0.8}{0.4} = 2$$
The law is therefore $y = 2.5\, x^2$

The remaining values can be calculated in a like manner.

x	0	0.5	1.0	1.5	2.0	2.5
y	0	5.73	11.46	22.39	43.76	85.51

2.12 The graph of $y = ae^{bx}$

A similar method to that used in Sec. 2.11 can be applied in this case.

Example

20. Draw the graph of $y = 3e^{1.34x}$ for values of x from $x = 0$ to $x = 2.5$

By logarithms
Equation: $y = 3e^{1.34x}$
Take logs of both sides:
$\log y = \log 3 + 1.34x \log e$
Note: $\log_{10} e = 0.4343$

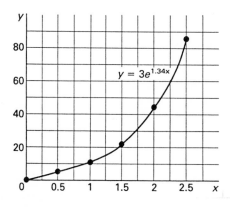

Figure 2.25

2.13 Exercises

1. Draw the graph of $y = 2.4x^{1.6}$ for values of x from $x = 0$ to $x = 5$.

2. Draw the graph of $y = 3x^{1.5}$ for values of x from $x = -10$ to $x = +10$.

3. Draw the graph of $y = 1.6x^{1.8}$ from $x = 0$ to $x = 6$. Use it to solve $1.6x^{1.8} = 8.5$.

4. Draw the graph of $2.5x^{2.5}$ from $x = 0$ to $x = 10$, and then solve the equation $2.5x^{2.5} - 12 = 0$.

5. The following values of x and y follow a law of the type $y = ax^n$.
   By plotting the graph of $\log y$ vertically against $\log x$ find values for a and n.

x	2	4	6	8	10
y	8	45	123.5	253	442.7

6. Plot the graph of $y = e^x$ for values of x from $x = -4$ to $x = +4$.

7. Plot the graph of $y = e^{-x}$ for values of x from $x = -10$ to $x = +10$.

8. Plot the graphs of $y = 2e^{-1.5x}$ at intervals of 0.5. From the graph determine (a) $2e^{-0.15}$ and (b) $2e^{+0.15}$.

9. Draw the graphs of the exponential functions given and use the graphs to determine (a) $2e^{-0.15}$ and (b) $2e^{+0.15}$.

   (a) $y = 4e^{0.5x}$ over a range $x = -4$ to $+4$ and determine the value of x when $y = 8$.
   (b) $y = \frac{2}{3}e^{-3x}$ over a range $x = -3$ to $+3$ and determine the value of y when $x = -2.75$ and the value of x when $y = 6$.
   (c) $y = 3e^{x^2}$ over a range $x = -2.5$ to $+2.5$ and determine the value of x when $y = 3.8$ and the value of y when $x = -2$.

   (d) $y = 1.5(1 - e^{-1.5x})$ over a range of $x = 0$ to $x = 2.5$ and determine the value of y when $x = 1.6$.
   (e) $y = \frac{1}{3}(e^x - e^{-x})$ over a range of $x = -4$ to $+4$ and determine the value of y when $x = +2.7$.

10. An experiment on a lamp gave the following measurements:

Voltage (V)	60	80	100	120	140	160
Luminosity (I)	10	31.6	88	184	322	580

Show that the law is of the type $I = aV^n$, where a and n are constants, and find the values of a and n.

(EMFEC)

11. Verify by means of a suitable graph that the values of x and y given in the following table approximately satisfy a law of the form $y = ke^{mx}$.

x	1	2	2.5	3	4	4.5
y	13.28	17.53	19.80	23.11	30.50	34.40

Find the values of k and m. (WJEC)

12. The table below shows the pressure and volume of a quantity of air when subjected to a moderately rapid compression.

Pressure (P)	15	30	60	100	200	400
Volume (V)	10.00	5.67	3.15	2.06	1.15	0.65

Show that P and V are connected by the law $PV^n = k$ and find the constants n and k. (WJEC)

34

13. The decay of voltage across a capacitor v_c at time t seconds is given by $v_c = Ve^{-t/CR}$. Draw a graph of decay when $CR = 20$ and $V = 500$ for a time range of $t = 0$ to $t = 60$ s.

14. A 4-microfarad capacitor is connected in series with a 1-megohm resistor across a 250-volt d.c. supply by means of a switch. Construct the graph of current against time during the charging period given that $i = Ie^{-t/CR}$ where $I = V/R$, Resistance R is measured in ohms, capacitance C is measured in farads, voltage V is measured in volts, and I is measured in amperes. Use a time scale of 0 to 20 seconds.

15. A coil of resistance 25 ohms and inductance 5 henrys is connected across a 100-volt supply by means of a switch. Construct a graph of current i against time t given that $i = I(1 - e^{-Rt/L})$ where $I = V/R$. Resistance R is measured in ohms, inductance L is measured in henrys, voltage V is measured in volts. Use a time scale of 0 to 1 second.

Answers

Exercises 2.3

1. (a) 20, positive
   (b) −4, positive
   (c) 25, negative
   (d) −15, positive
   (e) 4
   (f) 80, negative
2. $E = 0.005 L + 0.05$
3. $E = 0.3 W + 1.1$
4. $E = 0.2 W + 0.25$
   $W = 2.95, E = 2.25$
5. $c = 10.5, m = 7$
6. $a = 0.09, b = 18.4$
   $t = 125 °C$
7. 0.42, 7.5

8. 40, 0.03
9. 43, −8.5
10. 1.4, 2.6, 20.31
11. 4, −1.48
12. 0.6, 1.2
13. −0.77, 287
14. 0.5, 1.7
15. 2.4, −0.3
16. 4,7, 2.67
17. 12, −4

Exercises 2.7

1. (a) $x = 4, y = 3$
   (b) $x = 2, y = 3$
   (c) $x = 5, y = 6$
   (d) $x = 3, y = 1$
   (e) $x = 5, y = 6$
   (f) $x = 7, y = 8$
2. $x = 4, y = -1$
3. $x = 17, y = -19$
4. $x = 2, y = 3$
5,6,7,8. Graphs
9. (a) 10, −12
   (b) 8, −9
   (c) 1, 2
   (d) 9.3, 1.7
   (e) −1, −2
   (f) −1, −4
   (g) −5, −6
   (h) 1, 2
   (i) 1, 3
   (j) −⅓, 1
10. (a) 3, −6
    (b) 2, −7
    (c) 9, −4
    (d) 9, −8
    (e) 7, 6
    (f) 3 7
    (g) 4 3
11. −0.66, 2.66
12. 2.08, −2.88

Answers

Exercises 2.10

1. (a) 1.89
   (b) 1.0
   (c) 1.16
   (d) −1.21
   (e) 5.31
2. (a) 1, 1, −2
   (b) 1.69, 0.42, −2.11
   (c) 2.03, 0.37, −2.4
   (d) 1.62, 1, −0.62
   (e) 3.49, 0.34, −0.83
3. (a) 2, 1, −1
   (b) −0.8
   (c) 0.8, −0.55, −2.25
   (d) −0.4
   (e) 2, 0.6, −2.6
4. −0.57, 0.75, 2.3
5. −2.7, 0.55, 2.15
6. −1.4, 0.8, 3.6
7. (a) −1.7, 2.5, 5.2
   (b) −1.4, 1.9, 5.5
8. −1.56, 1.0
9. −1.25, 0.3, 2.0
10. −2.19, 0.78, 2.94

Exercises 2.13

1. Graph
2. Graph
3. 2.53
4. 1.873
5. 1.4, 2.5
6. Graph
7. Graph
8. 1.72, 2.32
9. (a) 1.39
   (b) 2552, 0.486
   (c) 164, 0.486
   (d) 1.36
   (e) 4.94
10. 0.000 000 434, 4.14
11. 10, 0.272
12. 1.189, 236
13. Graph
14. Graph
15. Graph

3 Mensuration

Mensuration is concerned with the measurement of perimeter, area, and volume.

3.1 The sphere

A sphere shown in Fig. 3.1 is a closed surface in which all the points are the same distance from a fixed point known as the centre.

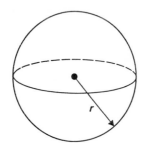

Figure 3.1

Volume of a sphere $= \frac{4}{3}\pi r^3$ where
r = radius of sphere
Surface area $A = 4\pi r^2$

Examples

1. Calculate the volume and total surface area of a sphere of diameter 20 m.
   Let $d = 20$ m then $r = 10$ m.
   Volume $= \frac{4}{3}\pi r^3 = \frac{4}{3} \times \pi \times 10^3 =$
   4189 m^3 correct to 4 significant figures.
   Surface area $= 4\pi r^2 = 4 \times \pi \times 10^2 =$
   1257 m^2 correct to 4 significant figures.

2. The volume of a sphere is 150000 mm^3. Calculate its diameter and total surface area.
   $V = 150000$ mm^3
   Volume: $V = \frac{4}{3}\pi r^3$

so radius $r = \sqrt[3]{\dfrac{3V}{4\pi}}$

$$r = \sqrt[3]{\frac{3 \times 150000}{4\pi}}$$

$$= \sqrt[3]{35810} = 33.00 \text{ mm}$$

Surface area: $A = 4\pi r^2$
$$= 4\pi \times 33^2$$
$$= 13685 \text{ mm}^2$$

The diameter of the sphere is 66 mm with a surface area of 13685 mm^2.

3.2 The cone

A cone has a circular base with sides evenly tapered to the top point as shown in Fig. 3.2.

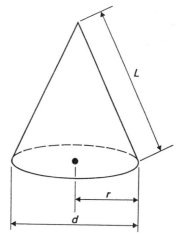

Figure 3.2

Volume of a cone $= \frac{1}{3}\pi r^2 h$
Curved surface area $= \pi r L$
Area of base $= \pi r^2$
Total surface area = curved surface area
$$+ \text{ area of base}$$
$$= \pi r L + \pi r^2$$
$$= \pi r(L + r)$$

Examples

3. An agricultural hopper has the form of an inverted cone of height 4 m and base diameter 2 m. Determine the volume of the hopper and its curved surface area.

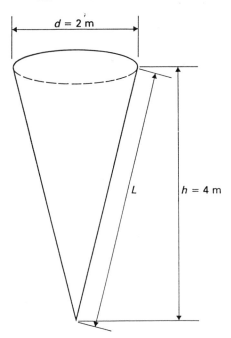

Figure 3.3

$d = 2$ m

$r = \dfrac{d}{2} = \dfrac{2}{2} = 1$ m

$h = 4$ m

Volume of hopper $= \tfrac{1}{3}\pi r^2 h$

$\qquad = \tfrac{1}{3} \times \pi \times 1^2 \times 4$

$\qquad = 4.189$ m^3

From theorem of Pythagoras:

$\quad L^2 = h^2 + r^2$

$\qquad = 4^2 + 1^2$

$\qquad = 16 + 1$

$\qquad = 17$

$\quad L = \sqrt{17} = 4.123$ m

Curved surface area $= \pi r L$

$\qquad = \pi \times 1 \times 4.123$

$\qquad = 12.95$ m^2

The volume of the hopper is 4.189 m^3 with a curved surface area of 12.95 m^2.

4. A conical heap of sand has a slant height of 3 m, and the circumference of the base is 11 m. Determine the volume of the sand and its total surface area.

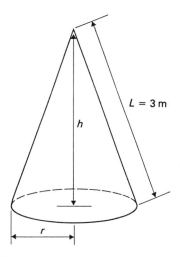

Figure 3.4

$L = 3$ m

Circumference $C = 11$ m

$\quad$ Circumference of a circle $= \pi d$

$$d = \frac{C}{\pi}$$

$d = \dfrac{11}{\pi} = 3.5$ m $\quad$ then $\quad r = \dfrac{d}{2} = \dfrac{3.5}{2}$

$\qquad = 1.75$ m.

Volume of cone $= \tfrac{1}{3}\pi r^2 h$

From theorem of Pythagoras:

$h^2 = L^2 - r^2$

$\qquad = 3^2 - 1.75^2$

$\qquad = 9 - 3.0625$

$\qquad = 5.9375$

$h \quad = 2.437$ m

Volume of cone $= \tfrac{1}{3}\pi r^2 h =$

$\tfrac{1}{3} \times \pi \times 1.75^2 \times 2.437 = 7.816$ m^3

Total surface area $= \pi r(L + r)$

$\qquad = \pi \times 1.75(3 + 1.75)$

$\qquad = \pi \times 1.75 \times 4.75$

$\qquad = 26.11$ m^2

The volume of sand is 7.816 m^3 with a total surface area of 26.11 m^2.

3.3 The pyramid

A pyramid is similar to a cone except that the base is a polygon as shown in Fig. 3.5. The sloping sides meet at the apex as shown in Fig. 3.6.

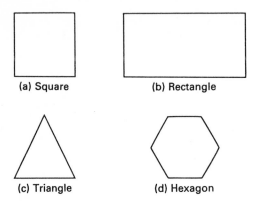

(a) Square   (b) Rectangle

(c) Triangle   (d) Hexagon

Figure 3.5

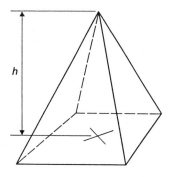

Figure 3.6

Volume of pyramid
= ⅓ area of base × perpendicular height
= ⅓Ah
Total surface area
= base area + lateral surface area

Example

5. Find the volume and total surface area of a prism with a square base of side 50 mm having a perpendicular height of 120 mm.
Area of base = 50 × 50 = 2500 mm^2
Volume of prism = ⅓Ah
           = ⅓ × 2500 × 120
           = 100000 mm^3
           = 100 cm^3
The sloping surface of the pyramid consists of four equal triangles as shown in Fig. 3.7. To find the area of one triangle we need to know the slant height L.

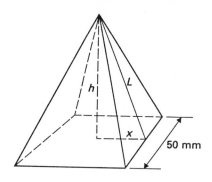

Figure 3.7

h = 120 mm x = 25 mm
By theorem of Pythagoras:
   $L^2 = h^2 + x^2$
       = 120^2 + 25^2
       = 14400 + 625
       = 15025
   L = 122.6 mm
Area of triangle = ½ base length × L
               = ½ × 50 × 122.6
               = 3065 mm^2
Lateral surface area = 4 × 3065 =
                   12260 mm^2

Total surface area
   = area of base + lateral surface area
   = 2500 + 12260
   = 14760 mm^2 = 147.6 cm^2
The volume of the prism is 100 cm^3 with a total surface area of 147.6 cm^2.

3.4 Frusta of cones and pyramids

A frustum of a cone or pyramid is the part that remains after the top has been removed by a cutting plane parallel to the base as shown in Fig. 3.8.

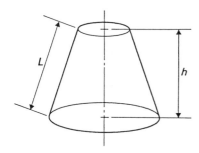

Figure 3.8

Volume of frustum $= \frac{1}{3}h(a + A + \sqrt{aA})$
where h = perpendicular height
$\quad a$ = area of top face
$\quad A$ = area of base
Curved surface area of cone =
$\frac{1}{2}L\pi\,(D + d)$
where d = diameter of top face
$\quad D$ = diameter of base
The lateral surface area of a pyramid = sum of the areas of the side surfaces.

Examples

6. Find the volume of a frustum of a cone with end diameters of 12 and 30 mm respectively with a perpendicular height of 40 mm.
d = 12 mm
D = 30 mm
h = 40 mm

Volume of frustum of cone
$= \frac{1}{3}h(a + A + \sqrt{aA})$

$= \frac{1}{3}h\left(\frac{\pi d^2}{4} + \frac{\pi D^2}{4} + \sqrt{\frac{\pi d^2}{4} \cdot \frac{\pi D^2}{4}}\right)$

$= \frac{\pi h}{12}\,(d^2 + D^2 + dD)$

$= \frac{40\pi}{12}\,(12^2 + 30^2 + [12 \times 30])$

$= 14\,703 \text{ mm}^3$

$= 14.7 \text{ cm}^3$

The volume of the frustum of the cone is 14.7 cm^3

7. An electrical terminal is in the shape of a frustum of a cone with dimensions as shown in Fig. 3.9.
Determine
(a) the volume of material,
(b) the mass of material if its density is 8 g/cm^3,
(c) curved surface area,
(d) total surface area.

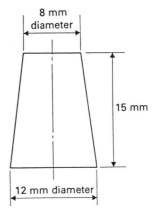

Figure 3.9

d = 8 mm
D = 12 mm
h = 15 mm

Volume $= \frac{\pi h}{12}\,(d^2 + D^2 + dD)$

$\qquad = \frac{15\pi}{12}(8^2 + 12^2 + [8 \times 12])$

$\qquad = 1194 \text{ mm}^3 = 1.194 \text{ cm}^3$

40

Mass = density × volume
= 8 × 1.194
= 9.552 g
Curved surface area = ½πL(D + d)

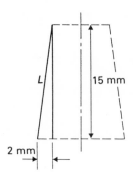

Figure 3.10

From Fig. 3.10: $L^2 = 15^2 + 2^2$
$= 225 + 4$
$= 229$
$L = 15.13$ mm
curved surface area = ½πL(D + d)
$= ½π × 15.13$
$(12 + 8)$
$= 475.3$ mm^2
Total surface area = area of base +
Area of top + curved surface area
$= \dfrac{πD^2}{4} + \dfrac{πD^2}{4} + 475.3$

$= \dfrac{π × 12^2}{4} + \dfrac{π × 8^2}{4} + 475.3$

$= 113.1 + 50.27 + 475.3$
$= 638.67$ mm
The volume of material is 1.194 cm^3 with
a mass of 9.552 g. The curved surface area
is 475.3 mm^2 with a total surface area of
638.67 mm^2.

8. A steel component is hexagonal in plane
and has the dimensions shown in Fig.
3.11.
Calculate (a) the volume of the component,
(b) its mass, given that the
density of steel is 7.8 g/cm^3

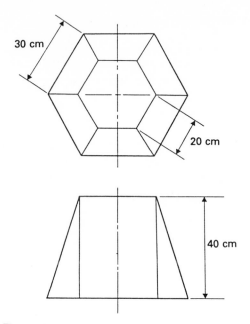

Figure 3.11

Volume of component =
$⅓h(a + A + \sqrt{aA})$
where $h = 40$ cm
a = area of top face
A = area of base
Consider the top face.

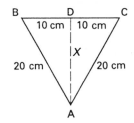

Figure 3.12

Area $a = 6 ×$ area of equilateral
triangle ABC
Area of triangle ABD = ½ × 10 × X
By theorem of Pythagoras:
$X^2 = 20^2 - 10^2$
$= 400 - 100$
$= 300$
$X = 17.32$ cm

Area of triangle ABD = ½ × 10 × 17.32 = 86.6 cm^2
Area of equilateral triangle = 2 × 86.6 = 173.2 cm^2
Area a = 6 × 173.2 = 1039.2 cm^2
Consider the base.

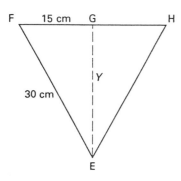

F   15 cm   G   H
30 cm
Y
E

Figure 3.13

By theorem of Pythagoras:
$$Y^2 = 30^2 - 15^2$$
$$= 900 - 225$$
$$= 675$$
$$Y = 25.98 \text{ cm}$$
Area of triangle EFG = ½ × 15 × 25.98 = 194.85 cm^2
Area of equilateral triangle EFH = 2 × 194.85 = 389.7 cm^2
Area A = 6 × 389.7 = 2338.2 cm^2
Volume of component
$$= \tfrac{1}{3}h(a + A + \sqrt{aA})$$
$$= \tfrac{1}{3} \times 40(1039.2 + 2338.2 + \sqrt{1039.2 \times 2338.2})$$
$$= 65816 \text{ cm}^3$$
Mass = density × volume = 7.8 × 65816
$$= 513364.8 \text{ g} = 513 \text{ kg.}$$
The component has a volume of 65816 cm^3 with a mass of 513 kg.

3.5 Volume of composite figures

A composite figure is one that consists of different parts; for example, a component may consist of a cone and a hemisphere in the form of a plumb-bob.

Examples

9. A solid plumb-bob is made up of a cone and hemisphere as shown in Fig. 3.14. Determine the volume of the plumb-bob.

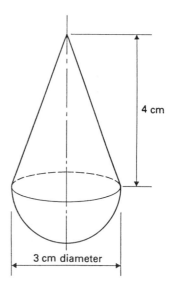

4 cm

3 cm diameter

Figure 3.14

Volume = volume of hemisphere + volume of cone
For cone: h = 4 cm, r = 1.5 cm
Volume of cone = $\tfrac{1}{3}\pi r^2 h$
$$= \tfrac{1}{3} \times \pi \times 1.5^2 \times 4$$
$$= 9.425 \text{ cm}^3$$
For hemisphere: r = 1.5 cm
Volume of hemisphere
= ½ volume of sphere
$$= \tfrac{1}{2} \times \tfrac{4}{3}\pi r^3$$
$$= \tfrac{1}{2} \times \tfrac{4}{3} \times \pi \times 1.5^3$$
$$= 7.069 \text{ cm}^3$$
Volume of plumb-bob
$$= 9.425 + 7.069$$
$$= 16.494 \text{ cm}^3$$
The volume of the plumb-bob is 16.494 cm^3.

10. Ten spheres of diameter 15 cm are being melted down and recast into four cones of diameter 20 cm. Determine the perpendicular height of each cone.

For sphere: $d = 15$ cm, $r = 7.5$ cm.

Volume of 10 spheres $= 10 \times 4/3\ \pi r^3$
$$= 10 \times 4/3 \times \pi \times 7.5^3$$
$$= 17\,672\ \text{cm}^3$$

Volume of 4 cones $= 17\,672\ \text{cm}^3$

Volume of one cone $= \dfrac{17\,672}{4}$

$$= 4418\ \text{cm}^3$$

For cone: $d = 20$ cm, $r = 10$ cm.

Volume of cone $= \frac{1}{3}\pi r^2 h$
$$h = \frac{3V}{\pi r^2}$$
$$= \frac{3 \times 4418}{\pi \times 10^2}$$
$$= 42.2\ \text{cm}$$

The height of each cone is 42.2 cm.

3.6 The ellipse

An ellipse is produced, as shown in Fig. 3.15, when a cone is cut by a plane at an angle to the base.

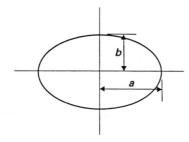

Figure 3.15

Area of ellipse $= \pi ab$
Perimeter of ellipse $= \pi(a + b)$
Volume $=$ area of ellipse $\times$ length

Example

11. A petrol tank is elliptical in cross section as shown in Fig. 3.16. Calculate the volume of the tank if it is 1.2 m long. Determine the amount of material used to construct such a tank assuming 10 per cent of material is used in joints and overlapping.

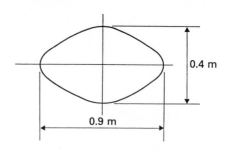

Figure 3.16

Length of major axes $= 0.9$ m, therefore $a = 0.45$ m
Length of minor axes $= 0.4$ m, therefore $b = 0.2$ m

Area of cross section $= \pi ab$
$$= \pi \times 0.45 \times 0.2$$
$$= 0.2827\ \text{m}^2$$

Volume of tank $= Ah = 0.2827 \times 1.2 = 0.34\ \text{m}^3$

Curved surface area of tank $=$ perimeter $\times$ length

Perimeter $= \pi(a + b)$
$$= \pi(0.45 + 0.2)$$
$$= 2.042\ \text{m}$$

Curved surface area $= 2.042 \times 1.2 = 2.4504\ \text{m}^2$

Total surface area $=$ area of two ends $+$ curved surface area
$$= (2 \times 0.2827) + 2.4504$$
$$= 0.5654 + 2.4504$$
$$= 3.0158\ \text{m}^2$$

Material used $= 3.0158 + 10\%$ of 3.0158
$$= 3.0158 + 0.301\,58$$
$$= 3.317\,38\ \text{m}^2$$

The volume of the tank is 0.34 m³ and the material needed was 3.32 m².

3.7 Exercises

1. Calculate the volume and surface area of a sphere of diameter 3 m.

2. Determine the volume and curved surface area of a cone when
   (a) $r = 20$ mm and $h = 150$ mm,
   (b) $r = 8$ cm and $h = 40$ cm,
   (c) $r = 1.2$ m and $h = 3$ m.

3. A cone of height 320 mm and base radius 70 mm is melted down and recast into a solid ball. Determine the diameter of the ball.

4. Two spheres of radius 75 and 50 mm, respectively, are to be replaced by a single sphere having the same volume as the two together. Determine the diameter of the single sphere.

5. A cylindrical boiler has hemispherical ends. The total length is 15 m and the diameter 2 m. Calculate the volume of the boiler and its total surface area.

6. Determine the volume of a square-based pyramid of perpendicular height 3 m if the length of one side of the base is 2 m.

7. Calculate the volume of the pyramids having bases as shown in Fig. 3.17, if the perpendicular height of each one is 5 m.

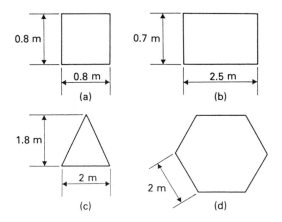

(a)

(b)

(c)

(d)

Figure 3.17

8. Calculate the mass of 500 ball-bearings of diameter 12 mm if 1 cm^3 of material has a mass of 7.5 g.

9. A navigation buoy consists of a cone mounted on a hemisphere. The total height is 4 m and the greatest diameter is 1.3 m. Calculate the volume of the buoy.

10. A bucket 400 mm high has a rim diameter of 250 mm and a base diameter of 160 mm. Determine the volume of water the bucket will hold.

11. A casting in the form of a frustum of a cone is 0.8 m long. The end diameters are 1 m and 0.5 m. Determine its mass if the density of the casting material is 2.7 g/cm^3.

12. A solid metal cone of diameter 80 cm and height 300 cm is melted down and recast into a frustum of a pyramid of base size 60×50 cm. Determine the perpendicular height of the pyramid if the top face size is 25×30 cm.

13. Calculate the cross-sectional area of an ellipse having a major axis of 4.5 m and a minor axis of 2.5 m.

14. An elliptical face plate has a maximum diameter of 200 mm and a minimum diameter of 150 mm. If its thickness is 20 mm determine (a) its volume and (b) its mass if 1 cm^3 of the face plate material has a mass of 7.85 g.

15. A hole of diameter 20 mm is bored through the centre of a sphere of diameter 100 mm. Calculate the remaining volume.

16. A storage tank is in the form of a horizontal cylinder with hemispherical ends. Total overall length is 2 m, with the length of the cylindrical portion being 1.1 m. Calculate the volume of the storage tank.

(WMAC)

17. A water storage tank is in the form of an inverted cone surmounted by a cylinder, the diameter of the cylinder and the cone being 2 m. The vertical heights of the cylindrical portion and the conical portion of the tank are 3 and 2.5 m, respectively. Determine the volume of the tank. Give the answer correct to two decimal places.

(WMAC)

18. A pyramid of vertical height 12 cm stands on a square base of side 10 cm. Find its volume and total surface area.

(EMFEC)

19. Calculate the volume of the light-alloy vee-pulley shown in Fig. 3.18.

(CGLI)

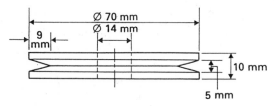

Figure 3.18

20. A casting takes the form of the frustum of a cone, the circles having radii of 2.8 and 1.4 m, the height being 1.2 m.
    (a) Calculate the volume.
    (b) An estimator incorrectly assumes that the volume is given by the product of the height and the area of the cross-section halfway up the height. Calculate the percentage error caused by adopting this incorrect method for this particular frustum.

21. The correct formula for the volume V of the frustum of a cone is

$$V = \frac{\pi h}{3} (R^2 + Rr + r^2).$$

Calculate the correct volume when $h = 6$ mm, $R = 14$ mm, and $r = 7$ mm.

Calculate the percentage error if the volume of such a frustum is taken as equivalent to a cylinder of the mean radius of 10.5 mm and the same height of 6 mm.

(CGLI)

22. If the lengths of the major and minor axes of an ellipse are a and b, the area of the ellipse is given by $\frac{\pi ab}{4}$. An ellipse has an area of 88 cm², the major axes being 6 cm longer than the minor axes. Find the length of the axes.

(CGLI)

23. (a) Find the volume of a circular cone of height 106 cm if the diameter of the base is 45 cm.
    (b) Find the diameter of the circular section of the cone parallel to its base and 36 cm from its vertex.

(NCFE)

24. A countersunk-head rivet is shown in Fig. 3.19. Determine the mass of 1000 such rivets if the density of the material used is 8.8 g/cm³.

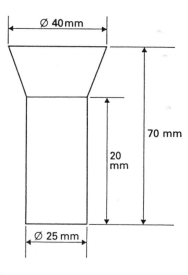

Figure 3.19

25. A dowel is shown in Fig. 3.20. Calculate the mass of 500 dowels if the density of material is 0.4 g/cm^3.

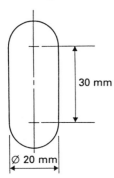

30 mm

Ø 20 mm

Figure 3.20

26. Figure 3.21 shows the frustum of a cone. Calculate the volume of the frustum.

(EMFEC)

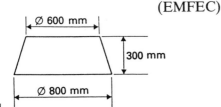

Ø 600 mm

300 mm

Ø 800 mm

Figure 3.21

27. A hot-water tank is in the shape of a vertical cylinder surmounted by a hemisphere. If the tank has a radius R and overall height h, write down a formula for calculating (a) the volume (b) the area of copper sheet required.

(EMFEC)

28. A hole was dug in the ground, square in plan, 3 m deep, with its sides sloping at 30° to the horizontal, as shown in Fig. 3.22.
    (a) If the bottom of the hole measures 2 × 2 m, calculate the dimensions of the hole at ground level.
    (b) The hole is to be used as a reservoir to store water. Calculate the area of plastic sheeting needed to cover the sloping sides and the bottom, and also the volume of water the hole will contain.

(EMFEC)

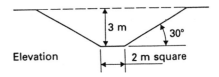

3 m   30°

Elevation   2 m square

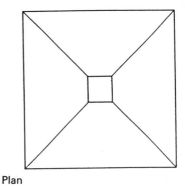

Plan

Figure 3.22

29. A right pyramid, standing on a square base of 50 mm side, has a perpendicular height of 100 mm. The top is cut off on a horizontal plane leaving a frustum of height 60 mm. Calculate the volume of the frustum and the surface area of one of the sloping sides.

(EMFEC)

30. A container in the form of a frustum of a cone is shown in Fig. 3.23. Calculate the volume of water in litres which the container will hold when full.

(EMFEC)

300 mm

300 mm

200 mm

Figure 3.23

31. A rectangular block of metal, 200 × 100 × 50 mm, is to be melted down and recast into a number of machine parts. Each part consists of a cone and a hemisphere joined together such that the base of the cone exactly fits the plane face of the hemisphere. The diameter of the joined face is 40 mm and the overall length of the part is 50 mm. Calculate (a) the total volume of each machine part, and (b) the number of complete machine parts that can be cast from the block of metal.

(EMFEC)

32. The volume of a sphere is 100000 mm^3. Calculate its diameter.

(EMFEC)

33. A cylinder 42 mm diameter and 30 mm long has a conical hole bored in the centre, 28 mm diameter on one side reducing to 21 mm diameter on the other side.
   (a) Calculate the volume of metal in the resulting solid.
   (b) In order to check the diameter of the hole, a 25 mm diameter sphere was pushed into the hole from the 28 mm diameter end, and the distance left projecting out of the hole, when firmly in contact with the conical sides, was measured. Determine this distance.

(EMFEC)

34. Figure 3.24 shows a solid piece of metal. It consists of section A, which is a cylinder, and section B, which is an inverted cone. Find the total volume contained in the metal.

(EMFEC)

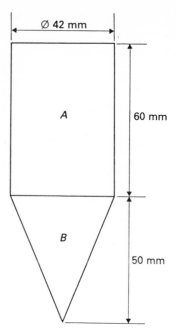

Figure 3.24

35. Figure 3.25 shows the section of an elecric motor housing; it is cylindrical in shape with the end a hollow hemisphere. Calculate the volume of the material in the casting. State your answer in cubic metres.

(EMFEC)

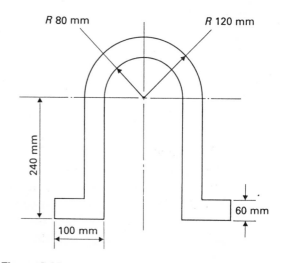

Figure 3.25

36. Figure 3.26 shows a component produced by a small engineering firm. Calculate the volume of metal used in its construction. All dimensions are in millimetres.

(EMFEC)

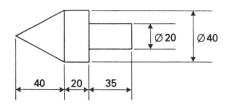

Figure 3.26

37. A right circular cone has the same radius r as the radius of a sphere and its volume is twice that of the sphere. Calculate the vertical height of the cone in terms of r.

(WMAC)

38. A crate contains steel ball-bearings each of ½ cm diameter. The total mass of the crate and its contents is 1600 g. If the crate has a mass of 69 g and 1 cm^3 of steel has a mass of 7.8 g, calculate the number of steel balls in the crate.

(NWRAC)

39. A sphere of diameter 254 mm has a conical hole in it whose apex is at the centre of the sphere and whose vertical angle is 90°. Find the volume of the remaining part of the sphere.

(WJEC)

40. A bucket in the shape of a frustum of a cone of end radii 250 and 100 mm and depth 375 mm, is filled to the top with water. The water is then used to fill a vessel in the shape of a sphere of radius 125 mm. Find the volume of water remaining in the bucket after the sphere is filled. What would be the radius of the spherical vessel if it just held all the water in the bucket?

(WJEC)

41. A square cylinder, i.e., of diameter equal to its length, is moulded into a sphere without loss of volume. Show that the reduction in surface area is approximately 13 per cent.

(CGLI)

3.8 Area of irregular figures. Mid-ordinate rule

To determine the area of Fig. 3.27 we can apply the mid-ordinate rule as follows:
(1) Draw the figure accurately;
(2) Choose an equal even number of strips, note the value of W;
(3) Draw in mid-ordinates y_1, etc;
(4) Measure the length of each mid-ordinate;
(5) Apply the formula:
$$\text{Area} = W(y_1 + y_2 + y_3 + y_4 + \ldots y_n)$$

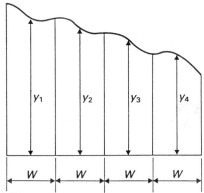

Figure 3.27

Example

12. An investigation gave the following results.

Force (N)	0	70	50	44	40	50	0
Distance (m)	0	2	4	6	8	10	12

Plot the graph of force against distance and from it determine the work done using the mid-ordinate rule.

Hint: The area under the curve represents the work done.

48

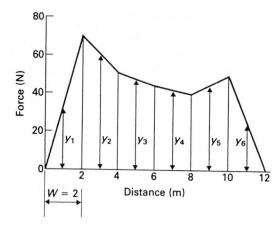

Figure 3.28

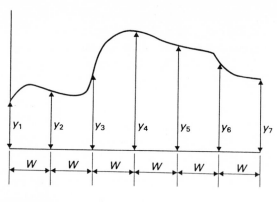

Figure 3.29

Area $= W(y_1 + y_2 + y_3 + y_4 + y_5 + y_6)$
$= 2(34 + 60 + 48 + 42 + 45 + 25)$
$= 2 \times 254$
$= 508 \text{ N m}$

The work done in this investigation was 508 N m.

3.9 Area of irregular figures. Trapezoidal rule

To determine the area of Fig. 3.29 we can apply the trapezoidal rule as follows:
(1) Draw the figure accurately;
(2) Choose an even number of strips, note the value of W;
(3) Draw in the ordinates y_1, etc. Note carefully the difference between this figure and Fig. 3.27;
(4) Measure the length of each ordinate;
(5) Apply the formula:

Area = strip width
$$\left[\left(\begin{array}{c} \text{average of first} \\ \text{and last ordinate} \end{array} \right) + \left(\begin{array}{c} \text{sum of all} \\ \text{other ordinates} \end{array} \right) \right]$$

Area =
$W\left[\tfrac{1}{2}(y_1 + y_7) + y_2 + y_3 + y_4 + y_5 + y_6\right]$

Example

13. A motor vehicle is slowing down from a velocity of 30 m/s to 10 m/s as shown in the table.

Time (s)	0	10	20	30	40	50	60
Velocity (m/s)	30	27	24	20	16	15	10

Use the trapezoidal rule to find the area under the curve thus giving the distance travelled by the motor vehicle.

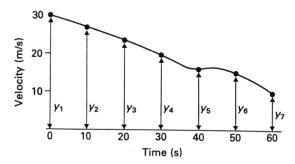

Figure 3.30

Area

$= W\left[\tfrac{1}{2}(y_1 + y_7) + y_2 + y_3 + y_4 + y_5 + y_6\right]$
$= \left[\tfrac{1}{2}(30 + 10) + 27 + 24 + 20 + 16 + 15\right]$
$= 10(20 + 27 + 24 + 20 + 16 + 15)$
$= 1220$

The distance travelled by the motor vehicle in slowing down was 1220 m.

3.10 Area of irregular figures. Simpson's rule

Simpson's rule is the most accurate of the formulae presented and combines the trapezoidal formula with the mid-ordinate formula. This rule demands an even number of strips.

$$\text{Area} = \frac{W}{3}(A + 2O + 4E)$$

where W = strip width
A = sum of first and last ordinates
O = sum of remaining odd ordinates
E = sum of all even ordinates

Example

14. The table gives values of x and y. Plot the graph and, using Simpson's rule, determine the area under the curve.

x	0	20	40	60	80	90
y	4	10	12	16	14	4

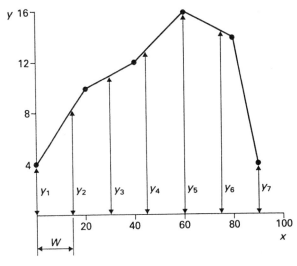

Figure 3.31

$$\text{Area} = \frac{W}{3}(A + 2O + 4E)$$
$$= \frac{W}{3}[(y_1 + y_7) + 2(y_3 + y_5) + 4(y_2 + y_4 + y_6)]$$
$$= \frac{15}{3}[(4 + 4) + 2(11 + 16) + 4(8.5 + 13 + 14.5)]$$
$$= 5(8 + 54 + 144)$$
$$= 1030$$

The area under the curve is 1030 units.

3.11 Volumes by Simpson's rule

To determine the volume of a solid, Simpson's rule can be applied. We use areas of parallel sections instead of lengths of ordinates. The section must still be divided into an even number of slices. Volume

$$= \frac{W}{3}\,(\text{sum of areas of ends}) + (2 \times \text{sum of odd areas}) + (4 \times \text{sum of even areas})$$

Example

15. The table gives the area of parallel sections of a precast component. Use Simpson's rule to determine its volume.

Distance from datum end (mm)	0	10	20	30	40	50	60
Area of cross section (mm^2)	7957	7382	4875	4465	3748	3297	1098

$$\text{Volume} = \frac{10}{3}[(7957 + 1098) + 2(4875 + 3748) + 4(7382 + 4465 + 3297)]$$
$$= \frac{10}{3}(9055 + 17246 + 60576)$$
$$= \frac{10}{3} \times 86877$$
$$= 289590 \text{ mm}^3$$

The volume of the precast component is 289590 mm^3.

3.12 Prismoidal rule

A prismoid is a solid three-dimensional figure having two parallel plane faces, for example, a frustum of a cone. The prismoidal rule is an adaptation of Simpson's rule where the solid is divided into two equal-width slices.

$$\text{Volume} = \frac{W}{3}(\text{area of one end } + \text{ area of other end } + 4 \times \text{ centre area})$$

Example

16. A component is shown in Fig. 3.32. Apply the prismoidal rule to determine its volume.

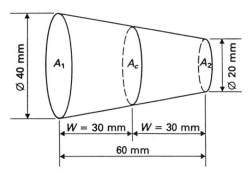

Figure 3.32

$$\text{Volume} = \frac{W}{3}(A_1 + A_2 + 4A_c)$$

If $D_1 = 40$ mm then

$$A_1 = \frac{\pi D_1^2}{4} = \frac{\pi \times 40^2}{4} = 1257 \text{ mm}^2$$

If $D_2 = 20$ mm then

$$A_2 = \frac{\pi D_2^2}{4} = \frac{\pi \times 20^2}{4} = 314 \text{ mm}^2$$

Centre diameter $= D_c = \frac{40 + 20}{2}$

$= 30$ mm

$$A_c = \frac{\pi D_c^2}{4} = \frac{\pi 30^2}{4} = 707 \text{ mm}^2$$

$$\text{Volume} = \frac{W}{3}(A_1 + A_2 + 4A_c)$$

$$= \frac{30}{3}(1257 + 314 + 4 \times 707)$$
$$= 10(1257 + 314 + 2828)$$
$$= 43\,990 \text{ mm}^3$$

The volume of the component is 43990 mm^3.

3.13 Theorem of Pappus for the volume of a solid

Pappus's theorem, sometimes referred to as Guldinus' theorem, states that the volume V of a solid of revolution is generated by rotating the area about an axis to develop the formula:

$$\text{Volume generated} = \text{area} \times \text{distance travelled by the centroid.}$$

To use the formula it is important that the axis of rotation must not pass through the area.

Full details of centres of mass can be found in Chapter 1 of *Physical Science and Physics Volume 1* of this series.

Examples

17. Find the mass of the ring that is shown in Fig. 3.33 if the density of the material is 7.7 g/cm^3.

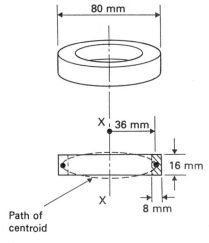

Path of centroid

Figure 3.33

Consider that the volume of the ring is made by one revolution of the cross-sectional area shown about the axis XX. Volume generated = area × distance travelled by centroid.

Area = 16 × 8 = 128 mm^2

Distance travelled = $2\pi r = 2\pi \times 36 =$ 226.2 mm

Volume generated = area × distance = 128 × 226.2 = 28953 mm^3

$\qquad\qquad\qquad = 29$ cm^3

Mass = density × volume = 7.7 × 29 = 223.3 g.

18. A vee is machined around the rim of a component as shown in Fig. 3.34. Calculate the volume of material removed in machining.

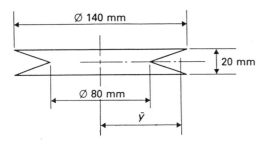

Figure 3.34

For a triangle: the position of the centre of the area is ⅓ of the perpendicular height.

Volume of material removed = area × distance travelled by centroid

Area of triangle
= ½ base × perpendicular height
= ½ × 20 × 30
= 300 mm^2

Distance travelled = $2\pi\bar{y}$

$\bar{y} = 70 - (⅓ \times 30)$
$\quad = 70 - 10$
$\quad = 60$ mm

Distance travelled = $2 \times \pi \times 60 =$ 377 mm

Volume of material removed = area × distance travelled

$= 300 \times 377$
$= 113100$ mm^3
$= 113.1$ cm^3

The volume of material removed is 113.1 cm^3.

3.14 Exercises

1. The following values of a variable force F corresponding to values of distance d moved through by a body are as follows:

Force (N)	0	22	45	64	52	40	30
Distance (m)	0	1	2	3	4	5	6

Draw the graph of F (vertical) against d (horizontal), and determine the work done using the mid-ordinate rule. The work done is the area under the graph.

2. The speed of a vehicle after starting from rest is given in the following table:

Time from rest (s)	0	5	10	15	20	25	30	35	40
Speed (m/s)	0	1.2	2.3	3.3	4	4.5	5	5.1	6

Plot the graph of speed (vertically) against time. Determine the area under the curve using the mid-ordinate rule and state what it represents. Find the total distance travelled in 40 seconds.

3. Sketch the curve $y = 25 - x^2$. Shade the area which lies between the x axis and the curve. Divide the area into 10 strips of equal width, calculate the mid-ordinates, and determine the shaded area using the mid-ordinate rule.

4. Draw a semicircle of radius 70 mm and use the mid-ordinate rule to determine its area. Compare the accuracy of this method with a calculated value.

52

5. A force varies with distance as shown in the table:

Force (N)	2	6	3	5	1	4	2
Distance (mm)	0	1	1.4	2.6	3.8	4.5	6

Plot a graph with distance on the horizontal axis. Use the trapezoidal rule to find the work done by the force which is equal to the area under the graph.

6. The current taken by a heater during an investigation is shown in the following table:

Current (A)	1.2	1.3	1.5	1.8	1.9	2.7	3.2
Time(s)	10	20	30	40	50	60	70

Plot a graph of time horizontally against current and, using the trapezoidal rule, determine the area under the curve. State the quantity found.

7. Draw a semicircle of radius 35 mm and using (a) the mid-ordinate rule (b) the trapezoidal rule, determine the area. Compare the accuracy of each method with the calculated value. State which method gives the more accurate value.

8. The table gives values of x and y.

x	0	1	2	3	4	5	6	7	8	9
y	2	4	7	10	15	25	32	36	45	50

Plot a graph and using Simpson's rule determine the area under the curve.

9. Plot the graph of $y = 8 + 2x - x^2$, between $x = -2$ and $x = 4$. Using Simpson's rule, calculate the area of part of the curve which lies above the x axis.

(NCFE)

10. Draw a semicircle of radius 50 mm and use Simpson's rule with (a) four, (b) eight, and (c) sixteen strips to determine its area. Check the accuracy of Simpson's result with that of a calculated value. Which number of strips gave the most accurate value?

11. Plot a graph of $y = \sin x$ for values of x from 0 to 180°. Use Simpson's rule to determine the area between the curve and the x axis.

12. In the following table are shown the values of A, the area in square centimetres of the cross-section of a body perpendicular to its axis, at a distance of x centimetres from one end:

Area (A)	80	110	120	114	90	62	45	22	10
Distance (x)	0	5.5	10	15	17.5	21	25	32	40

Plot a graph of area against distance as base and hence, using Simpson's rule with nine ordinates, find the volume of the body.

(NWRAC)

13. Find the volume of the circular ring shown in Fig. 3.35.

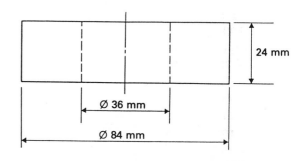

Figure 3.35

14. Calculate the mass of the ring shown in Fig. 3.36 if the density of the ring material is 8 g/cm^3.

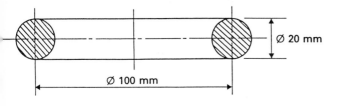

Figure 3.36

15. A shaft of 60 mm diameter is machined as shown in Fig. 3.37. Determine the volume of material removed in the semi-circular groove given the information in Fig. 3.38.

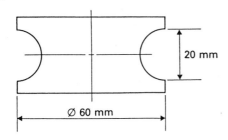

Figure 3.37

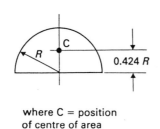

where C = position of centre of area

Figure 3.38

16. A groove of width 30 mm and of semi-circular cross-section is turned on a metal rod of 60 mm diameter. Determine the volume of metal removed.

17. A hollow ring has the cross-section shown in Fig. 3.39. Calculate the volume of material needed to cast 100 such rings.

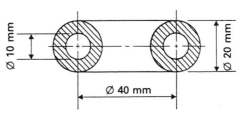

Figure 3.39

18. A pulley has dimensions as shown in Fig. 3.40. Calculate
    (a) the volume of material taken from the groove,
    (b) the volume of the pulley, and
    (c) its mass if the density of the material is 7.8 g/cm^3.

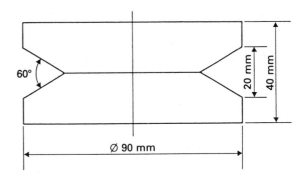

Figure 3.40

19. A storage bin has dimensions as shown in Fig. 3.41. Determine the volume of the bin using the prismoidal rule.

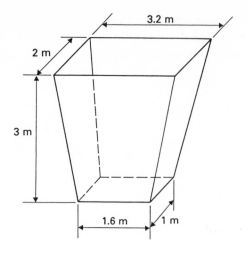

Figure 3.41

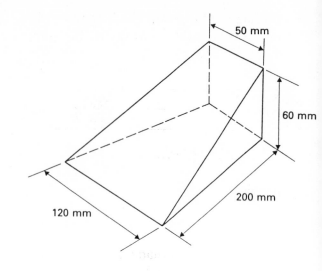

Figure 3.42

20. Calculate the volume of a rectangular hopper 1400 × 800 mm at the top and 1000 × 600 mm at the bottom. The hopper is 550 mm deep.

21. Calculate the volume of the frustum of a cone of height 4 m if the diameters of the faces are 1 and 3 m, respectively.

22. A machined component is 45 mm long with elliptical ends. At one end the major axis is 35 mm and the minor axis 20 mm, at the other 30 and 15 mm, respectively. Determine the volume of 1000 components.

23. A steel wedge has the dimensions shown in Fig. 3.42. Calculate the volume of material and its mass if the density of steel is 7.8 g/cm^3.

24. A shaper is used to machine the face of a casting. Due to variation in depth of cut, the force extended on the tool during a working stroke varies with distance moved, as below:

Distance moved by tool (mm)	0	50	100	150	200	225	250
Force on tool (N)	2800	3200	3600	4000	4400	4400	4400

Plot a graph showing the variation of force with position of tool and hence find the work done during each cutting stroke.

(NWRAC)

25. Find the volume generated when the area A, which is bounded by the curve $y = \sin x$, the x axis and the ordinates $x = \dfrac{\pi}{3}$, and $x = \dfrac{2\pi}{3}$ is rotated about the x axis.

(WJEC)

26. The velocity of a moving body at various times is given in the table:

Time (s)	0	1.5	2.8	3.6	5.0	6.2	7.7	8.9	10.3	12.0
Velocity (m/s)	33.7	31.5	27.5	25.4	22.4	20.3	18.2	16.9	15.8	15.0

Plot these points on a time base, and by using Simpson's rule with 12 strips, calculate the total distance covered during this particular 12 seconds.

(NCFE)

27. Sketch the curve $y = \frac{2}{3}\sqrt{36 - x^2}$ taking values of x at unit intervals from $x = 0$ to $x = 6$. Determine the area bounded by the curve and the x and y axes.

(NCFE)

28. If $y = 2x^3 - 3x^2 - 36x - 1$, find the area between the curve, the x axis, and the ordinates at $x = 1$ and $x = 3$.

(WJEC)

29. Find the area enclosed between the curve $y = 3x^2 + 5$, the x axis, and the ordinates at $x = 1$ and $x = 3$.

(WJEC)

30. In order to measure the volume of a tree trunk, 16 m long, the diameters of its ends and its circumference at equal intervals along its length were measured and are recorded below:

Distance along trunk (m)	0	4	8	12	16
Diameter (m)	1.2				0.6
Circumference (m)		3.2	2.7	2.2	

Calculate the volume of the trunk.

(EMFEC)

31. The following values give points on a curve:

x	4.5	5.6	6.5	7.4	8.6	9.5
y	0.3	0.8	1.6	2.6	3.9	5.3

Draw the curve on graph paper and read off the values of y when $x = 5, 6, 7, 8$, and 9. Use these values, together with Simpson's rule, to find the area under the curve between the limits $x = 5$ and $x = 9$.

(EMFEC)

32. An open channel, of varying depth, has a cross-section which is in the form of a trapezium whose horizontal base is 3 m and whose sides slope outwards at an angle 45° to the horizontal.

The following table shows the depth of the channel at sections taken at 5 m intervals along its length:

Length (m)	0	5	10	15	20
Depth (m)	6	4	4	3	2

Calculate the area at each cross-section and use Simpson's rule to calculate the volume of the channel.

(EMFEC)

33. A water tower 8 m high is circular in plan. The internal radius of the tower at varying heights is given in the table below:

Height (m)	0	2	4	6	8
Radius (m)	15	10	7	6	7

Calculate the area at each cross-section and, using Simpson's rule, calculate the volume of water in the tower when the depth of water is (a) 4 metres (b) 8 metres.

(EMFEC)

56

34. Figure 3.43 shows a symmetrical archway with dimensions.

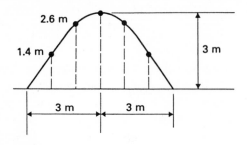

Figure 3.43

Determine, using Simpson's rule, the area of the archway.

(EMFEC)

35. Figure 3.44 shows the cross-section of a blank for a bevel gear. Use Pappus's theorem to calculate the mass of the blank if the density of the material from which it is made is 7.9 Mg/m^3.

(NCFE)

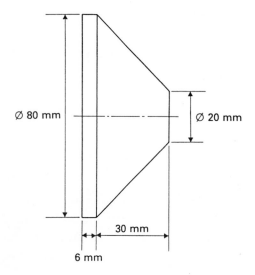

Figure 3.44

Answers

Exercises 3.7

1. 14.14 m^3
   28.27 m^2
2. (a) 62 832 mm^3
   9508 mm^2
   (b) 2681 cm^3
   1025 cm^2
   (c) 4.524 cm^3
   12.18 m^2
3. 146.4 mm
4. 163.6 mm
5. 45 m^3
   94.25 m^2
6. 4 m^3
7. (a) 1.066 m^3
   (b) 2.917 m^3
   (c) 3 m^3
   (d) 51.96 m^3
8. 3393 g
9. 2.057 m^3
10. 0.0134 m^3
11. 989.6 kg
12. 287 cm
13. 8.836 m^2
14. 471 cm^3
   3699 g
15. 20.98 cm^3
16. 0.318 m^3
17. 12.04 m^3
18. 400 cm^3
   360 cm^2
19. 31 997 mm^3
20. 17.24 m^3
   3.57 per cent
21. 2155 mm^3
   3.57 per cent
22. 14 cm
   8 cm
23. 15.28 cm
   56 195 cm^3
24. 364 582 g
25. 2723 g
26. 116 239 cm^3

27. Formula
28. 12.39×12.39
    43.17 m^2
    182.3 m^3
29. $98\,000 \text{ mm}^3$
    2433 mm^2
30. 0.1492 litres
31. 46.09 cm^3
    21
32. 28.79 mm
33. 4233 mm^3
    3.66 mm
34. $106\,217 \text{ mm}^3$
35. $20\,642 \text{ cm}^3$
36. $52\,883 \text{ mm}^3$
37. $h = 8r$
38. 2999
39. 7325 cm^3
40. $30\,109 \text{ cm}^3$
    20.91 cm
41. Proof

Exercises 3.14

1. 238 Nm
2. 142 m
3. 165
4. 7740 mm^2
5. 20.8 Nmm
6. 114 coulomb
7. 8 strips
   1951 mm^2
   1890 mm^2
   1924 mm^2
8. 152
9. 108

10. 3849 mm^2
    3875 mm^2
    3938 mm^2
    3927 mm^2
    16 strips
11. 11.48
12. 2622 cm^3
13. $108\,573 \text{ mm}^3$
14. $98\,696 \text{ mm}^3$
15. $25\,424 \text{ mm}^3$
16. $52\,496 \text{ mm}^3$
17. 2.96 m^3
18. $42\,692 \text{ mm}^3$
    $211\,777 \text{ mm}^3$
    1652 g
19. 11.2 m^3
20. 0.4657 m^3
21. 13.6 m^3
22. 3223 cm^3
23. 125 cm^3
24. 140 Nm
25. 3.01
26. 268 m
27. 18.8
28. 132
29. 36
30. 9.843
31.

x	y
5	0.5
6	1.15
7	2.15
8	3.25
9	6

32. 800 m^3
33. 352.9 m^3
    480 m^3
34. 11.2 m^2
35. 0.76 kg

4 Geometry and Trigonometry

Geometry is the study of properties and relations of figures in space, whereas trigonometry is the study of the relations between the sides and angles of triangles as applied to science and technology.

4.1 Degrees and radians

An angle is the amount of rotation between two straight lines and is measured in degrees, there being 360 degrees to a complete revolution. A radian is defined as the angle subtended at the centre of a circle by an arc equal in length to the radius of the circle, as shown in Fig. 4.1.

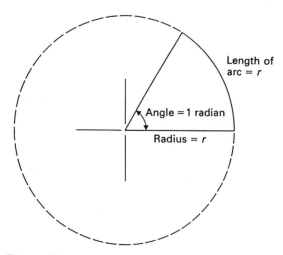

Figure 4.1

The circumference of a circle $= 2\pi r$, and its entirety subtends an angle of $360°$ at the centre.

Therefore 2π radians $= 360°$

$$1 \text{ radian} = \frac{360°}{2\pi} = 57.296°$$
$$= 57° \ 17' \ 45''$$

and 1 degree $= \dfrac{2\pi}{360}$ radians
$$= 0.01745 \text{ radians}$$

The abbreviation for radian is rad.

Examples

1. Convert $126°$ to radians.

$$1° = \frac{2\pi}{360} \text{ radians} = \frac{\pi}{180} \text{ radians}$$

$$126° = 126 \times \frac{\pi}{180} = 2.199 \text{ radians}$$

or
$$1° = 0.01745 \text{ radians}$$
$$126° = 126 \times 0.01745 \text{ radians} = 2.199 \text{ rad}$$

2. Express the given angle in radian measure.
   (a) $68° \ 54'$ (b) $52° 24' 35''$

   (a) $68° \ 54' = 68° + \dfrac{54°}{60} = 68.9°$

   $68.9° = 68.9 \times 0.01745$ radians
   $= 1.202$ rad.

   (b) $52° \ 24' \ 35'' =$

   $52° + \left[\dfrac{(24 \times 60) + 35}{3600} \right]° = 52.41°$

   $52.41° = 52.41 \times 0.01745$ radians
   $= 0.9146$ rad.

3. Without the use of tables convert (a) 3.864 radians to degrees and (b) $\frac{2}{3}\pi$ radians to degrees.
   (a) 1 radian $= 57.3$ degrees
   3.864 radians $= 3.864 \times 57.3$ degrees
   $= 221.4072$ degrees
   0.4072 degrees $= 0.4072 \times 60$
   $= 24.432$ minutes
   0.432 minutes $= 0.432 \times 60 = 26$ seconds correct to $1''$

Therefore 3.864 radians = 221°24′26″

(b) 1 radian = $\dfrac{180}{\pi}$

$\tfrac{2}{3}\pi$ radians = $\tfrac{2}{3}\pi \times \dfrac{180}{\pi}$ degrees

$\qquad = \tfrac{2}{3} \times 180$

$\qquad = 120$ degrees

Therefore $\tfrac{2}{3}\pi$ rad = 120°

4.2 Length of arc of a circle

From Fig. 4.1:

Length of arc for 1 radian = radius r radians
Length of arc for 2 radians = $\qquad 2r$ radians
Length of arc for 3 radians = $\qquad 3r$ radians
Length of arc for x radians = $\qquad xr$ radians

General formula:

$\quad$ Length of arc $S = xr$ radians

or

$\quad$ Length of arc $S = \dfrac{\pi x r°}{180}$

4.2 Area of sector of a circle

The sector of a circle is that part of a circle enclosed by an arc of a circle and two radii, as shown in Fig. 4.2

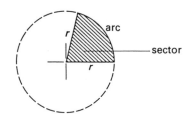

Figure 4.2

The area of a sector is proportional to the angle of rotation of the sector:

$\qquad$ Area of sector $A \propto x$ radians

Likewise

$\qquad$ Area of circle $\pi r^2 \propto 2\pi$ radians

Therefore $\quad A : \pi r^2 \quad$ as $\quad x : 2\pi$

so $\dfrac{A}{\pi r^2} = \dfrac{x}{2\pi}$

Area of sector $A = \dfrac{\pi r^2 x}{2\pi}$ where $\quad x \quad = $

angle in radians

$\qquad A = \dfrac{r^2 x}{2} \quad$ or $\quad \dfrac{\pi r^2 2x°}{360}$

Example

4. An arc of a circle, of diameter 200 mm, subtends an angle of 65°. Find the length of the arc and the area of the sector formed by the arc.

$d = 200$ mm therefore $r = 100$ mm
$x = 65°$

Length of arc $= \dfrac{\pi x° r}{180}$

$\qquad = \dfrac{\pi \times 65 \times 100}{180}$

$\qquad = 113.5$ mm

Area of sector $= \dfrac{\pi r^2 x°}{360}$

$\qquad = \dfrac{\pi \times 100^2 \times 65}{360}$

$\qquad = 5672.3$ mm^2

4.4 Exercises

1. Express the following angles in radian measure:
   (a) 76°; (b) 189°; (c) 345°;
   (d) 45° 16′; (e) 63° 56′;
   (f) 45° 37′ 34″; (g) 256° 43′ 23″;
   (h) 143° 46′ 36″.

2. Express each of the following angles in degrees:
   (a) 2π; (b) π; (c) $\tfrac{3}{4}\pi$; (d) $\tfrac{2}{3}\pi$; (e) $\tfrac{1}{2}\pi$;
   (f) $\tfrac{1}{4}\pi$; (g) 0.5; (h) 1.6; (i) 2.7; (j) 3.9;
   (k) 4.8 radians.

3. A wheel is turning at the rate of 54 revolutions per minute (r/min). Express this angular speed in radians per minute (rad/min).

4. A shaft is rotating at 100 r/min. Express this in radians per second (rad/s).

5. Calculate the length of an arc for a 50 mm diameter circle given the following angles:
   (a) 25°; (b) 75°; (c) 167°; (d) 247°; (e) 294°; (f) 0.58 rad; (g) 1.2 rad; (h) 1.65 rad; (i) 2.54 rad; (j) 3.62 rad.

6. Calculate the area of a sector formed by a circle of 125 mm diameter having the following angles:
   (a) 32°; (b) 86°; (c) 176°; (d) 234°; (e) 276°; (f) 0.2 rad; (g) 2.5 rad; (h) 3.65 rad; (i) 4.89 rad; (j) 5.5 rad.

7. Calculate the angle of lap if 580 mm of a belt are in contact with a pulley of diameter 250 mm.

8. A circle has a diameter of 300 mm. Find the angle at the centre subtended by an arc of length 120 mm.

9. The path of a pen in a mechanism is an arc of a circle of 350 mm radius subtending an angle of 70° at the centre of the circle. Calculate (a) the length of the path traversed by the pen, (b) the shortest distance between the two extreme positions of the pen.
   (WMAC)

10. A circular arc is 3.9 m long, the radius of the arc is 6.4 m. What is the angle subtended by the arc at the centre of the circle, in radians and degrees?
    What length of arc would subtend the angle of 70° in the same circle?
    (NWRAC)

11. A belt passing over a pulley 250 mm in diameter has 275 mm in contact with the pulley. Find (a) in radians (b) in degrees, the angle of lap of the belt on the pulley.
    (WMAC)

12. A water main is 500 mm diameter, and is more than half full of water. The angle subtended at the centre by the horizontal surface of the water is ⅔π radians. Calculate (a) the length of the circumference that is wetted (b) the depth of the water.
    (WMAC)

13. In a textile spinning machine a reciprocating arm swings forward and backward through an angle of 88°. The forward motion takes 2.5 seconds, the backward motion 11.5 seconds. Find the average number of radians per second during the forward and backward swings.
    (NWRAC)

14. The braking surface of a brake lining is in the form of an arc of a circle of radius 120 mm, and the angle subtended by the arc is 120°. Calculate the length of the braking surface.
    (YHCFE)

15. (a) A flywheel rotates 7 radians. How many complete revolutions does this represent?
    (b) Calculate the length of an arc of a circle 40 mm radius which subtends an angle of 0.5 radians at the centre.
    (EMFEC)

4.5 Solution of a right-angled triangle

'Solution of a triangle' means the determination of all its angles and the lengths of all its sides.
  Consider a triangle ABC as shown in Fig. 4.3.

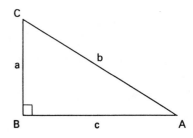

Figure 4.3

The sine of an angle is the ratio of the side opposite to the hypotenuse in a right-angled triangle.

That is,   sine $A = \dfrac{a}{b}$

The cosine of an angle is the ratio of the side adjacent to the hypotenuse in a right-angled triangle.

That is,   cosine $A = \dfrac{c}{b}$

The tangent of an angle is the ratio of the opposite side to the adjacent side in a right-angled triangle.

That is,   tangent $A = \dfrac{a}{c}$

The abbreviation for sine, cosine, and tangent are respectively sin, cos, and tan. Note that the expression $\sin^{-1} x$, $\cos^{-1} x$, and $\tan^{-1} x$ mean 'the angle whose sin (cos, tan) is x'.

Examples

5. In a triangle ABC, angle A = 38° and a = 85 mm. Find angle C if angle B is a right angle. Calculate the lengths b and c.

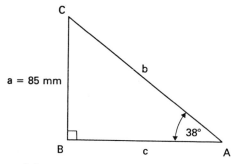

Figure 4.4

Angle C = 90° − 38° = 52°

$\sin A = \dfrac{a}{b}$, $\sin 38° = \dfrac{85}{b}$

$b = \dfrac{85}{\sin 38°} = \dfrac{85}{0.6157} = 138$ mm

$\tan A = \dfrac{a}{c}$, $\tan 38° = \dfrac{85}{c}$

$c = \dfrac{85}{\tan 38°} = \dfrac{85}{0.7813} = 108.8$ mm

Angle C = 52°, length b = 138 mm, and length c = 108.8 mm.

6. The hypotenuse of a right-angled triangle is 150 mm. If one angle is 23° determine the value of the other angle and the lengths of the other two sides.

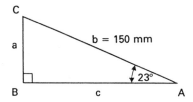

Figure 4.5

Angle C = 90° − 23° = 67°

$\sin A = \dfrac{a}{b}$, $\sin 23° = \dfrac{a}{150}$

$a = 150 \sin 23° = 150 \times 0.3907 = 58.61$ mm

$\cos A = \dfrac{c}{b}$, $\cos 23° = \dfrac{c}{150}$

$c = 150 \cos 23° = 150 \times 0.9205 = 138.1$ mm

Angle C = 67°, length a = 58.61 mm, and length c = 138.1 mm.

7. From Fig. 4.6 given that B = 90°, b = 15 m and a = 10 m, find the angles A and C and the length c.

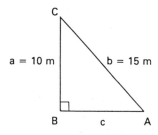

Figure 4.6

From Pythagoras: $b^2 = a^2 + c^2$
$$c^2 = b^2 - a^2$$
$$c^2 = 15^2 - 10^2$$
$$= 225 - 100$$
$$= 125$$
$$c = \sqrt{125} = 11.18$$

$\sin A = \dfrac{a}{b} = \dfrac{10}{15} = 0.6667$

Angle $A = \sin^{-1} 0.6667 = 41° 49'$
Angle $C = 90° - 41° 49' = 48° 11'$
Angle $A = 41° 49'$, angle $C = 48° 11'$, and length $c = 11.18$ m

8. From two points A and B, 100 metres apart, in a straight line with a tower, the angles of elevation of the top of the tower are 20 and 35°, respectively. Determine the height of the tower.

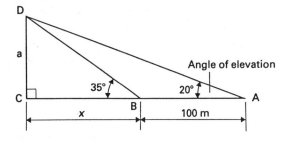

Figure 4.7

From triangle CBD,

$\tan 35° = \dfrac{a}{x}$, $a = x \tan 35°$

From triangle CAD,

$\tan 20° = \dfrac{a}{x + 100}$, $a = (x + 100) \tan 20°$

Therefore $x \tan 35° = (x + 100) \tan 20°$
$$0.7002x = 0.3640 \ x + 100 \times 0.3640$$
$$0.7002 \ x = 0.3640 \ x + 36.4$$
$$0.7002 \ x - 0.3640 \ x = 36.4$$
$$0.3362 \ x = 36.4$$
$$x = \dfrac{36.4}{0.3362}$$
$$= 108.3 \text{ m}$$

Substitute $x = 108.3$ in $a = x \tan 35°$
then $a = 108.3 \tan 35°$
$$= 108.3 \times 0.7002$$
$$= 75.83 \text{ m}$$
The height of the tower is 76 metres correct to 1 metre.

4.6 Exercises

1. Given a triangle ABC with angle B a right angle determine the lengths of the unknown sides for the following data:
   (a) $A = 47°$, $a = 25$ m
   (b) $A = 76°$, $b = 57$ m
   (c) $A = 42°$, $c = 97$ m
   (d) $C = 23°$, $a = 67$ m
   (e) $C = 65°$, $b = 33$ m
   (f) $C = 68°$, $b = 54$ m

2. Find the angles of a triangle ABC, given that angle $B = 90°$.
   (a) $a = 25$ m, $b = 54$ m
   (b) $a = 47$ m, $c = 34$ m
   (c) $b = 76$ m, $c = 54$ m
   (d) $b = 58$ m, $a = 28$ m
   (e) $c = 68$ m, $a = 32$ m
   (f) $c = 28$ m, $b = 50$ m

3. Calculate the angles of the isosceles triangle ABC shown in Fig. 4.8, given that $a = 16.2$ m and $c = 21.3$ m.

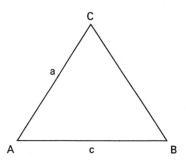

Figure 4.8

4. In a triangle ABC, $b = c = 450$ mm and $a = 160$ mm. Calculate angle A.

5. In a triangle ABC, b = c = 300 mm and angle A = 70°. Calculate length a.

6. In a triangle ABC, b = c and a = 120 mm. If angle A = 62° determine the length b.

7. A post 3 m tall is 20 m away from a tree 10 m high. Calculate the angle of elevation of the top of the tree from the top of the post.

8. From two points A and B, 250 metres apart, and in line with a building, the angles of elevation of the top of the building are 25° and 35°, respectively. Calculate the height of the building.

9. A man 2 metres tall is 30 metres away from a building 40 metres high. Determine the angle of elevation of the top of the building from the top of his head.

10. A flagstaff 6 metres high stands on the top of a building. From a point on the ground the angles of elevation of the top of the building and of the top of the flagstaff are 22° and 38°. Determine the height of the tower.

11. Figure 4.9 shows two pulleys A and B, of diameter 100 and 70 mm respectively, connected by an open belt. The centre distance between the pulleys is 140 mm.

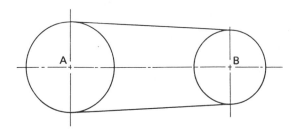

Figure 4.9

(a) Calculate the length of the belt assuming that it does not sag.
(b) If pulley A rotates at 210 rev/min, find the rotational speed of pulley B

assuming that no slip or creep occurs between the belt and the pulleys.
(WMAC)

12. ABC in Fig. 4.10 represents a seam of coal. If A is at a depth of 1000 m, determine to the nearest 10 m the depth of the seam at C.
(NWRAC)

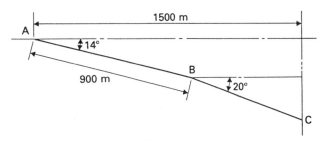

Figure 4.10

13. Two holes are to be located as shown at A and B in Fig. 4.11. Calculate the dimensions x and y from the two datum faces. All dimensions are in millimetres.
(WMAC)

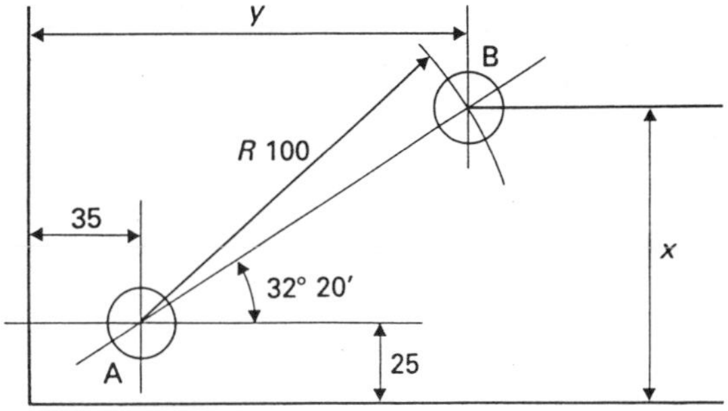

Figure 4.11

14. P and Q are points on a straight coastline, Q being 5.3 km east of P. A ship starting from P steams 4 miles in a direction 65½° north of east. Calculate:
(a) the distance the ship now is from the coastline.
(b) the ship's bearing from Q.
(NCFE)

64

15. A wire-forming machine produces components as shown in Fig. 4.12. Calculate how many components can be produced from 50 m of wire if 5 per cent of the wire is wasted in cutting off the components.

(NWRAC)

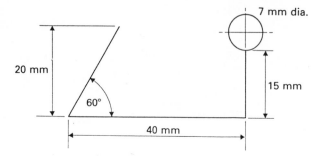

Figure 4.12

16. Assuming that the legs of a pair of dividers are 125 mm long and that they are set to scribe out a circle of 80 mm diameter:
    (a) Determine the included angle of the legs.
    (b) If the included angle is now adjusted to 12° 38′ what diameter of circle could now be scribed out?

(NCFE)

17. The diagonal of a rectangle 7 by 10 m makes an angle X with the longer sides. Calculate (a) angle X, (b) the length of the diagonal.

(NCFE)

18. An arrangement for checking the dimensions of a dovetail slide is shown in Fig. 4.13. Calculate the dimension x, to four significant figures, for the conditions shown. All dimensions are in millimetres.

(WMAC)

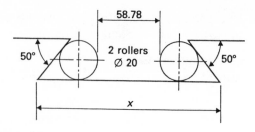

Figure 4.13

19. In a triangle ABC, AB = 3.5 m and AC = 1.7 m. The length of the perpendicular from B on to AC produced is 1.4 m. Calculate the length of BC.

(NWRAC)

20. A certain uniform incline rises 10.5 m in a length of 60 m along the incline. Find the angle between the incline and the horizontal.

Find also the rise of an incline of 100 m long which makes an angle of 20° with the horizontal.

(NWRAC)

21. (a) A wall is 7 m high. A ladder is placed with its foot 2 m from the foot of the wall. Calculate to the nearest 0.5 m the length of the ladder required to reach the top of the wall allowing 1.0 m extra for safety.
    (b) A man 1.8 m tall stands on horizontal ground and a lamp 7.0 m high casts a shadow of the man 3.0 m long. What is the distance from the man's foot to the foot of the lamp?

(NCFE)

22. Two gear wheels, of diameter 50 and 420 mm, are meshing together. If the larger gear wheel rotates through an angle of 120°, find the number of revolutions made by the smaller wheel.

(WMAC)

23. Figure 4.14 shows a tight cable AB, running from the top of a building to ground level, and passing over a wall D. Sag in the cable can be neglected.
    (a) Calculate
        (i) the length of the cable AB
        (ii) the angle of inclination θ
    (b) Using the properties of similar triangles, or otherwise, calculate
        (i) the vertical, clearance x
        (ii) the minimum clearance y beween the cable and the wall D.
                                                (CGLI)

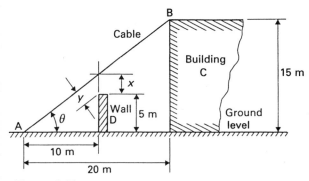

Figure 4.14

24. Three cylindrical plugs, each of diameter 40 mm, are placed in an equilateral triangular hole, each cylinder touching each other and being in contact with a side of the hole, as shown. Determine, by calculation, the length of the side of the triangular hole in millimetres, giving your answer to three significant figures.
                                                (WMAC)

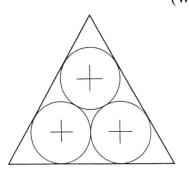

Figure 4.15

25. (a) In a triangle ABC, angle A = 90°, AB = 80 mm, BC = 250 mm. D is a point on AC such that angle ABD = 48°. Calculate
        (i) the length of AD correct to two decimal places;
        (ii) the angle ACB.
    (b) In a triangle ABC, angle B = 42°, AB = 210 mm, and AC = 380 mm. Calculate
        (i) the perpendicular distance from A to BC;
        (ii) the angle ACB.
                                                (WMAC)

26. Two cables, 20 and 10 m long, are required for the temporary support of a concrete column as shown in Fig. 4.16. Determine the distance between the anchor points A and B.
                                                (EMFEC)

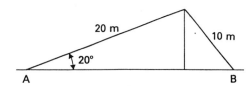

Figure 4.16

27. ABC is a triangle in which the side AB is 4 m long and the angles B and C are 43 and 55°, respectively. The perpendicular from A to BC meets BC at D. Calculate the lengths of AD, BD, and BC. Give the answers correct to three places of decimals.
                                                (WMAC)

28. A ladder 6.1 m long rests against a vertical wall. By means of trigonometrical tables find the inclination of the ladder to the horizontal when the foot of the ladder is:
    (a) 2.15 m from the wall;
    (b) 3.1 m from the wall.

Use these angles to calculate how far the top of the ladder descends when the ladder is moved from its first to its second position.

(NCFE)

29. In Fig. 4.17 ABCD is a sketch of part of a regular hexagon and EBCF, part of a regular octagon. Calculate the size of the angle ABE.

(NCFE)

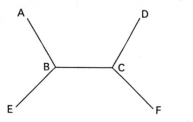

Figure 4.17

30. (a) Using trigonometrical tables find the value of (i) sin 60° 29′, (ii) cos 8° 11′, (iii) tan 36° 53′.
    (b) Figure 4.18 shows an aerial mast XC 350 m high. A and B are two points due west of the mast at the same horizontal levels as C. If the angle of elevation of X from A is 35° and from B is 62°, calculate the distance from A to B.

(CGLI)

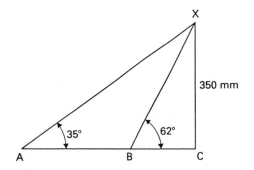

Figure 4.18

31. Referring to the template shown in Fig. 4.19, calculate, giving your answers to the nearest millimetre
    (a) the coordinates of point E (i.e., the distances indicated by x and y);
    (b) the distance CD;
    (c) the distance ED.
    All dimensions are in millimetres.

(CGLI)

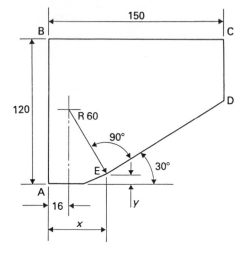

Figure 4.19

32. In a survey a point C is observed from two other points A and B, 300 m apart. The angles ABC and BAC are found to be 45° and 60° respectively. Calculate the length of AC and the shortest distance from C to AB.

(NWRAC)

33. The angle of elevation of the top of a vertical tower at a horizontal distance of 100 m from the foot of the tower is 56°. Calculate (a) the height of the tower, (b) the angle of elevation of the top of the tower from a point whose horizontal distance from the tower is 200 m and whose height above the horizontal plane through the foot of the tower is 55 m.

(NCFE)

34. Triangle ABC is right-angled at B, with AB = 5.2 cm, BC = 3.9 cm. BD is the perpendicular from B to AC meeting AC in D. Calculate the lengths of the sides BD, AD, DC, and the area of the triangle ABC.

35. Figure 4.20 shows a theoretical metric thread cut in a nut.
    (a) The M5 metric thread has a major diameter of 5 mm and a pitch of 0.8 mm. Calculate the theoretical minor diameter.
    (b) A useful way of selecting tapping drills for metric threads is to use a drill of diameter equal to the major diameter minus the pitch. If this method is used for the M5 thread calculate.
    (i) the actual depth of thread in the nut
    (ii) the percentage ratio of the actual depth to the theoretical depth.
    (CGLI)

Calculate
(a) the distance AC
(b) the distance CO
(c) the distance CP_1
(d) the time available during which articles can be lifted from the conveyer belt.
(CGLI)

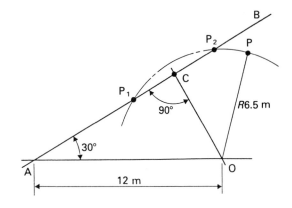

Figure 4.21

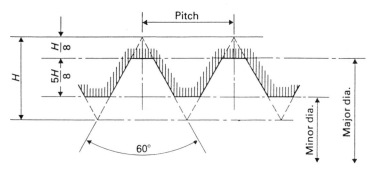

Figure 4.20

36. In Fig. 4.21, AB represents the path of **articles** on a conveyor belt. OP repre-**sents the maximum lift radius of the arm of a crane, pivoted at O, so that articles can be lifted from the conveyor belt** between points P_1 and P_2. Articles move along the conveyor at a speed of 2 m/min.

37. Figure 4.22 illustrates the position of two radar stations A and B which have located a ship C. Station B is 400 km east 55° north from A, C is 800 km south 42° east from B. Calculate: (a) the distances OA, OP, OQ, and AC; (b) the angle PAC.
(CGLI)

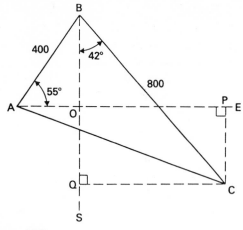

Figure 4.22

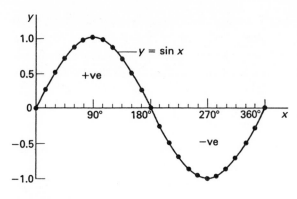

Figure 4.23

38. From the top of a lighthouse, 40 metres above the sea, the angle of depression of a boat is 17°. Calculate how far the boat is from the lighthouse.

39. A person on the top of a cliff 30 m high observes that the angle of depression of a buoy at sea is 13°. How far is the buoy from the cliff.

40. A person on the top of a cliff 33 m high is in line with two buoys whose angles of depression are 16° 30′ and 11° 20′. Determine the distance between the two buoys.

4.7 Graphs of trigonometrical functions: $y = \sin x$

A graph of $y = \sin x$ is plotted as shown in Fig. 4.23.

From the graph:
(a) all values of sin x lie between -1 and $+1$;
(b) for angles between 0 and 180° values of sin x are positive;
(c) for angles between 180 and 360° values of sin x are negative.

4.8 Graphs of trigonometrical functions: $y = \cos x$

A graph of $y = \cos x$ is plotted as shown in Fig. 4.24.

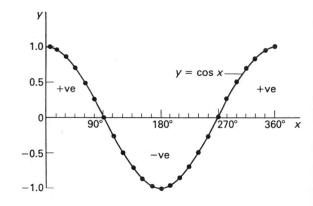

Figure 4.24

From the graph:
(a) all values of cos x lie between -1 and $+$ 1;
(b) for angles between 0 and 90° values of cos x are positive;
(c) for angles between 90 and 270° values of cos x are negative;
(d) for angles between 270 and 360° values of cos x are positive.

4.9 Graphs of trigonometrical functions: $y = \tan x$

A graph of $y = \tan x$ is shown in Fig. 4.25.

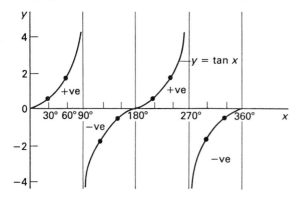

Figure 4.25

The shape of the graph for $y = \tan x$ can be seen to be different to that of $y = \sin x$ and $y = \cos x$. The sine and cosine graphs are continuous and repeat themselves at intervals of 360°, but the tangent graph is discontinuous and repeats itself at intervals of 180°.

From the graph:
(a) values of $\tan x$ can be greater than ±1;
(b) for angles between 0 and 90° values of $\tan x$ are positive;
(c) for angles between 90 and 180° values of $\tan x$ are negative;
(d) for angles between 180 and 270° values of $\tan x$ are positive;
(e) for angles between 270 and 360° values of $\tan x$ are negative.

4.10 Values of $\sin x$, $\cos x$ and $\tan x$ for angles between 0 and 360°, using a calculator

Examples

9. By using a calculator determine the sine, cosine, and tangent of the following angles:
   (a) 76°; (b) 104°; (c) 207°; (d) 309°.

(a) sin 76°
   Key operation: 76 sin   Readout: 0.970295726
   cos 76°
   Key operation: 76 cos   Readout: 0.241921895
   tan 76°
   Key operation: 76 tan   Readout: 4.010780934
   For practical purposes the readout values would be corrected to four decimal places.
(b) sin 104°
   Key operation: 104 sin   Readout: 0.970295726
   cos 104°
   Key operation: 104 cos   Readout: −0.241921895
   tan 104°
   Key operation: 104 tan   Readout: −0.010780934
(c) sin 207°
   Key operation: 207 sin   Readout: −0.453990499
   cos 207°
   Key operation: 207 cos   Readout: −0.891006524
   tan 207°
   Key operation: 207 tan   Readout: −0.509525449
(d) sin 309°
   Key operation: 309 sin   Readout: −0.777145961
   cos 309°
   Key operation: 309 cos   Readout: −0.629320391
   tan 309°
   Key operation: 309 tan   Readout: −1.234897157

10. Determine the cosine of 153° 22′ 16″
    cos 153° 22′ 16″
    Key operation: 16 ÷ 3600 + 22 ÷ 60 + 153 = cos
    Readout: −0.89392836

4.11 Values of sin x, cos x and tan x for angles between 0 and 360°, using tables

The information deduced from the graphs in Sec. 4.7 can be calculated as follows:

Angle x	$\sin x$	$\cos x$	$\tan x$
0	0	1	0
Between 0 and 90	+	+	+
90	1	0	∞
Between 90 and 180	+	−	−
180	0	−1	0
Between 180 and 270	−	−	+
270	−1	0	∞
Between 270 and 360	−	+	−
360	0	+1	0

Figure 4.26 reduces this table to a less complicated picture.

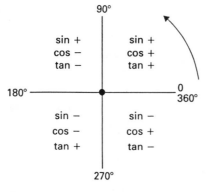

Figure 4.26

A further reduction is shown in Fig. 4.27 which replaces the signs of sine, cosine, and tangent with the letters CAST.

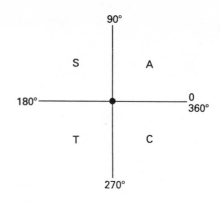

Figure 4.27

A means that all values are positive,
C means that only the cosine is positive,
S means that only the sine is positive,
T means that only the tangent is positive.

Example

11. Determine the sine, cosine, and tangent of the following angles, using tables:
    (a) 100°; (b) 200°; (c) 300°.
    (a) When using tables, angles in the second quadrant are always deducted from 180°.
    sin 100° = +sin (180 − 100)° =+
    sin 80° = 0.9848
    cos 100° = −cos (180 − 100)° =−
    cos 80° = −0.1736
    tan 100° = −tan (180 − 100)° =−
    tan 80° = −5.6713
    (b) When using tables, angles in the third quadrant always have 180° deducted.
    sin 200° = −sin (200 − 180)° =−
    sin 20° = −0.3420
    cos 200° = −cos (200 − 180)° =−
    cos 20° = −0.9397
    tan 200° = +tan (200 − 180)° =+
    tan 20° = +0.3640

(c) When using tables, angles in the fourth quadrant are always deducted from 360°.

$\sin 300° = -\sin (360 - 300)° = -\sin 60° = -0.8660$

$\cos 300° = +\cos (360 - 300)° = +\cos 60° = +0.5$

$\tan 300° = -\tan (360 - 300)° = -\tan 60° = -1.7321$

4.12 Exercises

1. Draw a graph of $y = \sin \theta$ for values of θ from 0 to 360°.

2. Sketch the graphs of the following between $x = 0°$ and $x = 360°$:
   (a) $y = 2 \sin x$; (b) $y = \sin 0.5\,x$; (c) $y = 3 \sin 2x$.

3. Draw a graph of $y = \cos \theta$ for values of θ from 0 to 360°.

4. Sketch the graphs of the following between $x = 0°$ and $x = 360°$:
   (a) $y = \cos 0.5x$; (b) $y = 2 \cos x$; (c) $y = 0.5 \cos 2x$.

5. Draw a graph of $y = \tan x$ for values of x from $x = 0$ to $x = 360°$.

6. Use a calculator to determine values of sine, cosine, and tangent of:
   (a) 66°; (b) 104°; (c) 285°; (d) 305°;
   (e) 160° 25′; (f) 234° 54′; (g) 345° 36′;
   (h) 167° 43′ 23″; (i) 246° 54′ 26″

7. Calculate the values of sine of the following, using a calculator:
   (a) ½π; (b) ⅓π; (c) ⅔π; (d) ¾π;
   (e) ¼π; (f) ⅛π; (g) ⅜π; (h) ⅝π; (i) ⅞π
   radians.

8. By using tables, determine the sine, cosine, and tangent of the following angles:
   (a) 176°; (b) 94°; (c) 189°; (d) 265°;
   (e) 279°; (f) 340°.

4.13 The sine rule

Consider the triangle ABC shown in Fig. 4.28. Draw a perpendicular from B to AC. Let BD = h

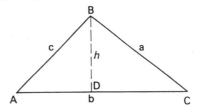

Figure 4.28

From triangle ABD: $\sin A = \dfrac{h}{c}$
then $h = c \sin A$

From triangle BCD: $\sin C = \dfrac{h}{a}$
then $h = a \sin C$

Therefore $c \sin A = a \sin C$

$$\frac{a}{\sin A} = \frac{c}{\sin C}$$

In a similar manner by drawing the perpendicular from A to BC:

$$\frac{b}{\sin B} = \frac{c}{\sin C}$$

Therefore:

$$\frac{a}{\sin A} = \frac{b}{\sin B} = \frac{c}{\sin C}$$

Example

12. Solve the triangle ABC, given that A = 80°, C = 48° 18′ and b = 160 mm.

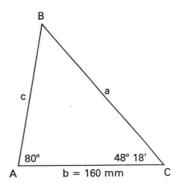

Figure 4.29

Angle A + angle B + angle C = 180°
Angle B = 180 − (angle A + angle C)
$$= 180° - (80° + 48° \, 18')$$
$$= 180 - 128° \, 18'$$
$$= 51° \, 42'$$

From $\dfrac{a}{\sin A} = \dfrac{b}{\sin B}$ $\quad a = \dfrac{b \sin A}{\sin B} =$

$$\dfrac{160 \sin 80°}{\sin 51° \, 42'} = 200.8 \text{ mm}$$

From $\dfrac{a}{\sin A} = \dfrac{c}{\sin C}$ $\quad c = \dfrac{a \sin C}{\sin A} =$

$$\dfrac{200.8 \sin 48° \, 18'}{\sin 80°} = 152.2 \text{ mm}$$

The complete solution is a = 200.8 mm, c = 152.2 mm, and B = 51° 42'.

13. Solve the triangle ABC, given that c = 8.5 m, b = 7.3 m and B = 42°.

From $\dfrac{b}{\sin B} = \dfrac{c}{\sin C}$ $\quad \sin C = \dfrac{c \sin B}{b}$

$$\dfrac{8.5 \sin 42°}{7.3} = 0.7791$$

Therefore angle C = $\sin^{-1} 0.7791$ = 51° 11'.

Angle A + angle B + angle C = 180°
Angle A = 180° − (angle B + angle C)°
$$= 180° - (42° + 51° \, 11')$$
$$= 180° - 93° \, 11'$$
$$= 86° \, 49'$$

From $\dfrac{a}{\sin A} = \dfrac{b}{\sin B}$ $\quad a = \dfrac{b \sin A}{\sin B} =$

$$\dfrac{7.3 \sin 86° \, 49'}{\sin 42°} = 10.89 \text{ m}$$

The complete solution is a = 10.89 m, A = 86° 49', and C = 51° 11'.

4.14 The cosine rule

By inspection it can be seen that the sine rule cannot be used in the solution of triangles given:

(a) the dimensions of three sides;
(b) the dimensions of two sides and the angle between them;
(c) two angles and the dimensions of the sides joining them.

A further rule called the cosine rule is developed using the theorem of Pythagoras to help with the solution of such triangles. Consider the triangle ABC as shown in Figure 4.30. Draw a perpendicular from B to AC. Let BD = h.

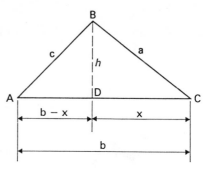

Figure 4.30

From triangle BCD: $h^2 = a^2 - x^2$
From triangle ABD: $h^2 = c^2 - (b - x)^2$
Therefore $a^2 - x^2 = c^2 - (b - x)^2$
$$a^2 - x^2 = c^2 - (b^2 - 2bx + x^2)$$
$$a^2 - x^2 = c^2 - b^2 + 2bx - x^2$$
$$a^2 = c^2 - b^2 + 2bx$$

From triangle BCD: $\cos C = \dfrac{x}{a}$ $\quad x = a \cos C$

Substitute $x = a \cos C$ into $a^2 = c^2 - b^2 + 2bx$

then $a^2 = c^2 - b^2 + 2ba \cos C$
then $c^2 = a^2 + b^2 - 2ab \cos C$

By using a similar method we can show that:
$$a^2 = b^2 + c^2 - 2bc \cos A$$
$$b^2 = a^2 + c^2 - 2ac \cos B$$

Examples

14. Find the angles of the triangle whose sides are 46, 36, and 54 metres long respectively.

Let a = 46 m, b = 36 m, and c = 54 m.
From $a^2 = b^2 + c^2 - 2bc \cos A$

$$\cos A = \frac{b^2 + c^2 - a^2}{2bc}$$

$$\cos A = \frac{36^2 + 54^2 - 46^2}{2 \times 36 \times 54} = 0.5391$$

$$A = \cos^{-1} 0.5391 = 57.38° = 57° \ 23'$$

$$\cos B = \frac{a^2 + c^2 - b^2}{2ac}$$

$$= \frac{46^2 + 54^2 - 36^2}{2 \times 46 \times 54} = 0.7520$$

$$B = \cos^{-1} 0.7520 = 41.24° = 41° \ 14'$$

Angle C = 180° − (angle B + angle A)°
$= 180° - (41° \ 14' + 57° \ 23')$
$= 180° - 98° \ 37'$
$= 81° \ 23'$

The angles of the triangle are 57° 23′, 41° 14′, and 81° 23′.

15. Given that a = 41.4 cm, b = 68.4 cm, and C = 41° 37′, solve the triangle ABC.
From the cosine rule:
$c^2 = a^2 + b^2 - 2ab \cos C$
$\quad = 41.4^2 + 68.4^2 - 2 \times 41.4 \times 68.4 \cos 41° \ 37'$
$\quad = 6392$
$c = 79.95$ cm

From $\dfrac{a}{\sin A} = \dfrac{c}{\sin C}$ $\quad \sin A = \dfrac{a \sin C}{c} =$

$$\frac{41.4 \sin 41° \ 37'}{79.95} = 0.3456$$

$A = \sin^{-1} 0.3456 = 20.22° = 20° \ 13'$
Angle B = 180° − (angle A + angle C)°
$= 180° - (20° \ 13' + 41° \ 37')$
$= 118° \ 10'$
The complete solution is c = 79.95 cm, A = 20° 13′, and B = 118° 10′

4.15 Exercises

Solve the following triangles assuming that lengths a, b, and c are measured in metres.
1. a = 5, b = 7, and A = 43°.
2. a = 27, b = 44, and B = 62°.
3. a = 31, A = 42°, and B = 54°.
4. b = 243, c = 194, and B = 72°.
5. b = 201, c = 242, and C = 82°.
6. b = 72, B = 87°, and C = 46°.
7. c = 85, B = 114°, and C = 43°.
8. a = 85, B = 29°, and C = 65°.
9. b = 29, A = 82°, and B = 44°.
10. b = 32, A = 75°, and B = 64°.
11. a = 31, b = 48, and c = 50.
12. a = 42, b = 175, and c = 180.
13. a = 54, b = 114, and c = 110.
14. a = 42, b = 48, and C = 135°.
15. b = 20, c = 12, and A = 47°.
16. a = 32, c = 52, and B = 100°.
17. a = 270, b = 330, and c = 194.
18. a = 180, b = 220, and c = 127.
19. a = 110, b = 120, and c = 210.
20. a = 5.5, b = 6.5, and C = 32°.
21. b = 104, c = 62, and A = 50°.
22. a = 152, b = 132, and B = 96°.

Use the sine rule and cosine rule to solve the following:

23. In the triangle ABC angle A = 30°, side b = 10 cm, and side c = 18 cm. Calculate the angles B and C, the length of a, and the area of the triangle.

(NWRAC)

24. In a triangle ABC, AB = 15 cm, AC = 18 cm, and angle ABC = 52°. Calculate angle ACB.

(EMFEC)

25. An aerial mast is erected on a roof sloping at 13° to the horizontal, as

shown in Fig. 4.31. One of the supporting wires is fixed to the mast at A and to the roof at C. If AB is 8 m and BC is 10 m, calculate the length of the stay AC and the angle it makes with the mast.

(EMFEC)

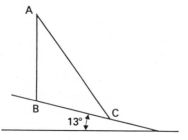

Figure 4.31

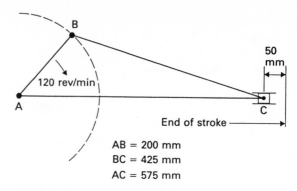

AB = 200 mm
BC = 425 mm
AC = 575 mm

Figure 4.32

26. KLM are three terminals on a base board, forming an acute-angled triangle with KL = 75 mm, LM = 50 mm, and angle LKM = 35°. Calculate the length of MK.

(WJEC)

27. In a triangle ABC, BC = 100 mm, AB = 150 mm, and angle A = 30°. Show, in two sketches, that this information provides data for two triangles and calculate the two possible values for the third side.

(NWRAC)

28. In the crank and connecting rod mechanism of a feed mechanism shown in Fig. 4.32, the crank rotates at 120 r/min. For the position indicated, i.e., when the crosshead is 50 mm from dead centre, calculate:
(a) the crank angle A;
(b) the time it will take the crosshead to travel a further 50 mm to reach dead centre.

(CGLI)

29. Two forces acting on a body are shown in Fig. 4.33. Calculate the resultant of these two forces.

(EMFEC)

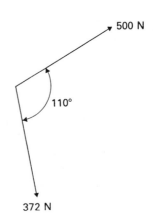

Figure 4.33

30. Two forces, F1 = 40 kN and F2 = 60 kN, are shown in Fig. 4.34. Calculate the resultant of these (i.e., length AB) and the angle this makes with F1.

(EMFEC)

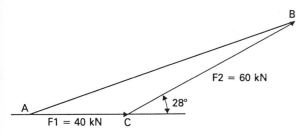

Figure 4.34

31. Figure 4.35 shows a 30 m high vertical mast AB restrained by taut guy wires BC and BD which make angles of 30° to the vertical, such that points C, A, and D are in line. The ground plane slopes as indicated and the distance AD is 18 m. Calculate (a) the length of both guy wires BC and BD, (b) the distance AC.

(EMFEC)

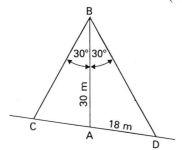

Figure 4.35

32. A jib crane consisting of a tie AB and a strut BC is fixed to two points CA fastened to a vertical post (point C is at ground level). AB = 10 m, BC = 15 m, and CA = 12 m. Sketch the jib crane and calculate the height of the point B above ground level and the horizontal distance of point B from the wall.

(EMFEC)

33. In a survey a point C is observed from two other points A and B, 300 m apart. The angles ABC and BAC are found to be 45 and 60°, respectively. Calculate the length of AC and the shortest distance from C to AB.

(NWRAC)

34. In a reciprocating engine the lengths of the crank AC and the connecting rod AB are 1 and 4.8 m respectively. Calculate the value of angle ABC to the nearest degree, when the angle ACB is 86°.

(NWRAC)

35. In the layout shown in Fig. 4.36 A and B represent the centres of two gears. An idler is to be positioned with its centre at C so that AB = 21 units, AC = 10 units, and CB = 17 units. Use the cosine rule to calculate the magnitude of angle CAB and the lengths x and y.

(CGLI)

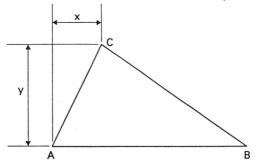

Figure 4.36

36. Calculate, using the information in Fig. 4.37, (a) the checking distance x between the centres of the two holes, (b) the angle marked B.

(CGLI)

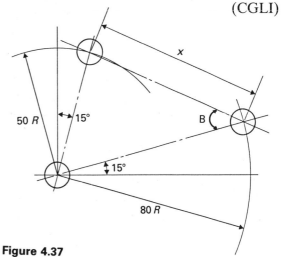

Figure 4.37

37. Four straight members of a mechanism form a quadrilateral ABCD. AB = 4 m, BC = 12 m, CD = 2 m, DA = 11 m, and the angle ADC = 130°. Calculate the angle BAD.

(NWRAC)

38. In Fig. 4.38, A and B represent the centres of two gears. An idler is to be positioned with its centre at C so that AC = 90 mm and CB = 80 mm. Calculate (a) the distance AB, (b) the angle BAC, (c) angle CBA.

(CGLI)

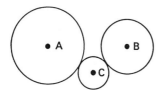

Figure 4.38

39. Figure 4.39 shows one panel of a pin-jointed framework, the panel being in the form of a parallelogram. Calculate the length of the diagonal BD to three significant figures.

(CGLI)

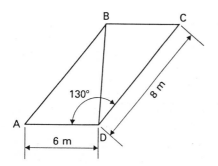

Figure 4.39

40. Three holes are to be drilled in a casting as shown in Fig. 4.40. Calculate the jig boring dimensions x and y.

(NWRAC)

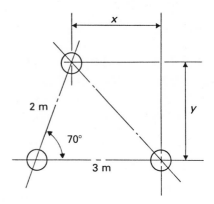

Figure 4.40

41. A metal plate is in the shape of a triangle ABC where angle ABC = 42°. The corner at B is rounded off by an arc of a circle of radius 2.5 cm, the sides BA and BC being tangential to the arc. If AB = 28 cm and BC = 20 cm (measurements being taken to the point B before the corner was rounded off) determine the perimeter of the plate.

(WJEC)

42. Two alternating quantities are represented by vectors of lengths 25 and 50, which act at the same point. The angle between the vectors is 60°. Calculate the resultant quantity and the angle it makes with the larger of the original quantities.

(WMAC)

43. A circular plate has a diameter AB and O is the centre of the circle. Two holes centres C and D are marked on the plate on pitch circles of radius 5.4 and 6.8 cm, respectively, and on the same side of AB. Angle COA is 21° and angle DOB is 57°. Calculate the length CD and the angle of inclination of CD to AB.

(NWRAC)

44. Figure 4.41 shows the relationship between a tower C and two observation positions A and B. Determine the distances d and h.

(EMFEC)

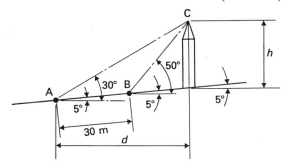

Figure 4.41

4.16 Area of a triangle

In general terms the area of any triangle is half the product of the base and perpendicular height.

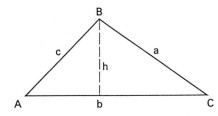

Figure 4.42

From Fig. 4.42:
Area of triangle = ½bh
From this formula two others can be developed for the area of a triangle.

From Fig. 4.42:

$$\sin A = \frac{h}{c} \quad \text{so } h = c \sin A$$

Substitute $h = c \sin A$ into area = ½bh, then area = ½bc sin A. The third formula is long and complicated to derive but useful:

Area of triangle = $\sqrt{s(s-a)(s-b)(s-c)}$
where $s = ½(a + b + c)$.

Examples

16. Calculate the area of a triangle ABC given b = 5 m, c = 8 m, and A = 65° 24′.

Area of triangle = ½bc sin A
= ½ × 5 × 8 × sin 65° 24′
= 18.19 m^2

17. In the triangle ABC, B = 50°, a = 6 m, and c = 8 m. Calculate the area of the triangle and angles A and C.

Area of triangle = ½ac sin B
= ½ × 6 × 8 × sin 50°
= 18.39 m^2

From the cosine rule:
$$b^2 = a^2 + c^2 - 2ac \cos B$$
$$= 6^2 + 8^2 - (2 × 6 × 8 × \cos 50°)$$
$$= 38.29$$
$$b = 6.19 \text{ m}$$

From the sine rule:
$$\frac{b}{\sin B} = \frac{c}{\sin C} \quad \text{so } \sin C = \frac{c \sin B}{b} =$$
$$\frac{8 \sin 50°}{6.19} = 0.9900$$

Angle C = $\sin^{-1}$ 0.9900 = 81° 54′.
Angle A + angle B + angle C = 180°
Angle A = 180° − (angle B + angle C)°
= 180° − (50° + 81° 54′)
= 48° 06′

18. The sides of a triangle ABC are a = 5.8 m, b = 8.2 m, and c = 10.3 m. Calculate the angle B and the area of the triangle.

Area of triangle

$$= \sqrt{s(s - a)(s - b)(s - c)}$$

$$s = \tfrac{1}{2}(5.8 + 8.2 + 10.3) = 12.15$$

$$\text{Area} = \sqrt{12.15(12.15 - 5.8)(12.15 - 8.2)(12.15 - 10.3)}$$

$$= \sqrt{12.15 \times 6.35 \times 3.95 \times 1.85}$$

$$= \sqrt{563.792}$$

$$= 23.74 \text{ m}^2$$

From the cosine rule:

$$\cos B = \frac{a^2 + c^2 - b^2}{2ac}$$

$$= \frac{5.8^2 + 10.3^2 - 8.2^2}{2 \times 5.8 \times 10.3} = 0.6067$$

Angle B = $\cos^{-1} 0.6067 = 52° 39'$.

4.17 Exercises

Solve the following triangles ABC and find the area of each triangle. Assume the length dimensions to be metres.

1. a = 11, b = 15, C = 57°.
2. b = 62, c = 41, A = 65°.
3. a = 20, c = 13, B = 39°.
4. a = 32, b = 44, C = 104°.
5. b = 10, c = 8, A = 60°.
6. a = 2, c = 3, B = 112°.
7. a = 4, b = 2, c = 3.
8. a = 6, b = 3, c = 7.
9. a = 8, b = 5, c = 9.
10. A = 35°, B = 75°, b = 4.6.
11. A = 72°, B = 35°, a = 24.
12. A = 112°, C = 21°, a = 16.
13. A = 79°, C = 54°, c = 32.
14. B = 108°, C = 69°, b = 24.
15. B = 121°, C = 17°, c = 44.

Use the sine rule, cosine rule, and area of a triangle formula to solve the following problems:

16. If the area of a triangle is 100 m² and two of its sides are 21 m and 15 m, find the angle between these sides.

17. A triangle, whose sides are 14.5, 33.6 and 37.4 cm, respectively, is made of a material whose mass per square centimetre is 16 g. Determine the mass of the triangle.

18. Figure 4.43 shows a triangle ABC having sides AB and BC both equal to 2 units. The perpendicular height is $\sqrt{3}$ units. Calculate the area of the triangle.
(EMFEC)

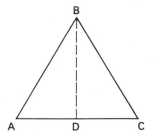

Figure 4.43

19. A triangular hole is cut in a rectangular plate as shown in Fig. 4.44. The plate is 5 mm thick. Calculate (a) the area of the triangular hole, (b) the mass of the remaining plate in kilograms if the density of material is 7800 kg/m³.
(EMFEC)

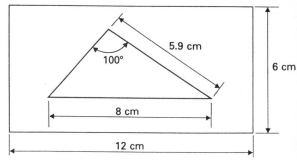

Figure 4.44

20. In a triangle ABC side a = 25 mm, side b = 10 mm, and angle B = 19°. Show that there are two possible triangles and calculate the area of each. (EMFEC)

21. Calculate the area of a triangle if two of its sides have lengths of 20 and 50 mm, respectively, and the sine of the angle at their intersection is 0.7.

(EMFEC)

22. A triangle has sides of length 5.2 and 2.5 m forming an obtuse angle. If the area of the triangle is 3.3 m², calculate the length of the third side and the size of all three angles in degrees.

(EMFEC)

23. The plan of a building plot is a quadrilateral ABCD in which AB = 50 m, BC = 60 m, CD = 32 m, DA = 42 m, and the diagonal BD = 66 m. Calculate the area of the plot of land.

(EMFEC)

24. Calculate the area of the building plot shown in Fig. 4.45 to the nearest square metre.

(EMFEC)

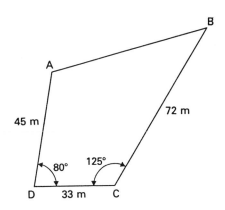

Figure 4.45

25. The field ABCD shown in Fig. 4.46 is surveyed, and the lengths measured are recorded below:
AB = 75 m, BC = 99 m, CD = 189 m, DA = 75 m, AC = 156 m.
The field is to be divided into two parts of equal area by a straight-line fence AX.

Determine the distance CX and the length of the fence AX.

(EMFEC)

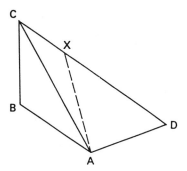

Figure 4.46

4.18 Complementary angles

Consider the triangle ABC in Fig. 4.47

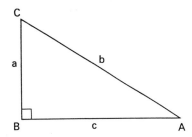

Figure 4.47

When two angles together make 90°, the angles are said to be complementary. Therefore angles A and C are complementary, that is, angle A + angle C = 90°.

From the ratios of a right-angled triangle,

$$\sin A = \frac{a}{b} \quad \cos A = \frac{c}{b}, \text{ and } \tan A = \frac{a}{c}$$

$$\sin C = \frac{c}{b} \quad \cos C = \frac{a}{b}, \text{ and } \tan C = \frac{c}{a}$$

It can be seen that $\sin A = \frac{a}{b}$ and $\cos C$

$= \frac{a}{b}$, therefore $\sin A = \cos C$

But angle C = 90 − A; therefore sin A = cos (90 − A).

Now, cos A = $\dfrac{c}{b}$ and sin C = $\dfrac{c}{b}$; therefore cos A = sin C

But angle C = 90 − A; therefore cos A = sin (90 − A).

4.19 The ratios of 30, 45 and 60°

Consider the isosceles triangle in Fig. 4.48.

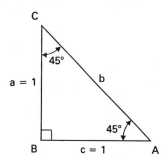

Figure 4.48

From Pythagoras:
$$b^2 = a^2 + c^2$$
$$= 1^2 + 1^2$$
$$= 1 + 1$$
$$= 2$$
$$b = \sqrt{2}$$

From the triangle BAC: sin A = $\dfrac{a}{b} = \dfrac{1}{\sqrt{2}}$

That is, sin 45° = $\dfrac{1}{\sqrt{2}}$

cos A = $\dfrac{c}{b} = \dfrac{1}{\sqrt{2}}$

That is, cos 45° = $\dfrac{1}{\sqrt{2}}$

tan A = $\dfrac{a}{c} = \dfrac{1}{1}$

That is, tan 45° = $\dfrac{1}{1} = 1$

Summary: tan 45° = 1, sin 45° = $\dfrac{1}{\sqrt{2}}$

and cos 45° = $\dfrac{1}{\sqrt{2}}$

Consider the equilateral triangle in Fig. 4.49

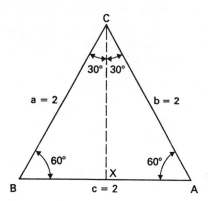

Figure 4.49

Since CBX and CAX are concurrent, XA = 1

By Pythagoras:
$$CX^2 = AC^2 - AX^2$$
$$= 2^2 - 1^2$$
$$= 4 - 1$$
$$= 3$$
$$CX = \sqrt{3}$$

From the ratio definitions:

sin 60° = $\dfrac{CX}{AC}$

$= \dfrac{\sqrt{3}}{2}$

cos 60° = $\dfrac{AX}{AC}$

$= \dfrac{1}{2}$

tan 60° = $\dfrac{CX}{AX}$

$= \dfrac{\sqrt{3}}{1}$

Summary: sin 60° = $\dfrac{\sqrt{3}}{2}$

cos 60° = ½, and tan 60° = $\sqrt{3}$

From the ratio definitions:

$$\sin 30° = \tfrac{1}{2}$$
$$\cos 30° = \frac{\sqrt{3}}{2}$$
$$\tan 30° = \frac{1}{\sqrt{3}}$$

summary: $\sin 30° = \tfrac{1}{2}$, $\cos 30° = \dfrac{\sqrt{3}}{2}$, and $\tan 30° = \dfrac{1}{\sqrt{3}}$

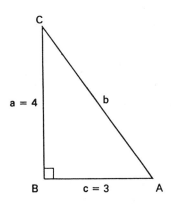

Figure 4.50

4.20 The reciprocal of sine, cosine, and tangent

The reciprocal of sine is the cosecant, i.e.,

$$\frac{1}{\sin x} = \text{cosecant } x.$$

The reciprocal of cosine is the secant, i.e.,

$$\frac{1}{\cos x} = \text{secant } x.$$

The reciprocal of tangent is cotangent, i.e.,

$$\frac{1}{\tan x} = \text{cotangent } x.$$

The abbreviations for cosecant, secant, and cotangent are, respectively, cosec, sec, and cot. Note that the reciprocal of sine is cosecant and the reciprocal of cosine is secant, which is the opposite to what you might have expected.

Examples

16. Given that $\tan x = \dfrac{4}{3}$, find the value for $\sin x$ and $\cos x$.

From Fig. 4.50: given $\tan x = \dfrac{4}{3}$, then

$a = 4$ and $c = 3$.

By Pythagoras:
$$\begin{aligned} b^2 &= a^2 + c^2 \\ &= 4^2 + 3^2 \\ &= 16 + 9 \\ &= 25 \\ b &= 5 \end{aligned}$$

Therefore $\sin x = \dfrac{a}{b} = \dfrac{4}{5}$ and

$$\cos x = \frac{c}{b} = \frac{3}{5}$$

17. Without the use of tables, write down the following values:

(a) $\dfrac{\sin 40°}{\cos 50°}$ (b) $\dfrac{\sec 20°}{\text{cosec } 70°}$

(a) From complementary angles:
$\cos 50° = \sin (90° - 50°) = \sin 40°$

Therefore $\dfrac{\sin 40°}{\cos 50°} = \dfrac{\sin 40°}{\sin 40°} = 1$

(b) $\dfrac{\sec 20°}{\text{cosec } 70°} = \dfrac{\dfrac{1}{\cos 20°}}{\dfrac{1}{\sin 70°}} = \dfrac{\sin 70°}{\cos 20°}$

From complementary angles:
$\cos 20° = \sin (90° - 20°) = \sin 70°$

Therefore $\dfrac{\sec 20°}{\text{cosec } 70°} = \dfrac{\sin 70°}{\cos 20°}$

$= \dfrac{\sin 70°}{\sin 70°} = 1$

18. Without using tables, given that sec x = $\frac{15}{12}$, find sin x, cos x, tan x, cosec x, and cot x.

sec $x = \dfrac{1}{\cos x}$; therefore $\cos x = \dfrac{1}{\sec x}$

$= \dfrac{1}{\frac{15}{12}} = \dfrac{12}{15}$

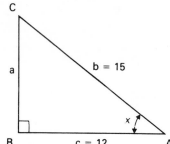

Figure 4.51

From Fig. 4.51: given $\cos x = \dfrac{12}{15}$,   then $c = 12$ and $b = 15$.

By Pythagoras: $a^2 = b^2 - c^2$
$\qquad\qquad\quad = 15^2 - 12^2$
$\qquad\qquad\quad = 225 - 144$
$\qquad\qquad\quad = 81$
$\qquad\qquad a = 9$

So $\sin x = \dfrac{9}{15}$, $\tan x = \dfrac{9}{12}$, $\mathrm{cosec}\, x = \dfrac{15}{9}$

and $\cot x = \dfrac{12}{9}$

4.21 Trigonometrical identities

1. From Fig. 4.52: $\sin A = \dfrac{a}{b}$, $\cos A = \dfrac{c}{b}$,

and $\tan A = \dfrac{a}{c}$

Now $\dfrac{\sin A}{\cos A} = \dfrac{\frac{a}{b}}{\frac{c}{b}} = \dfrac{a}{b} \times \dfrac{b}{c} = \dfrac{a}{c}$

but $\tan A = \dfrac{a}{c}$

So $\tan A = \dfrac{\sin A}{\cos A}$

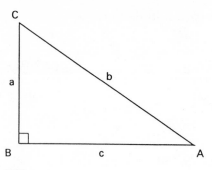

Figure 4.52

2. Because $\cot A = \dfrac{1}{\tan A}$ then $\cot A$

$= \dfrac{1}{\frac{\sin A}{\cos A}} = \dfrac{\cos A}{\sin A}$

3. By Pythagoras: $a^2 + c^2 = b^2$

Divide both sides by b^2: $\dfrac{a^2 + c^2}{b^2} = \dfrac{b^2}{b^2}$

$\dfrac{a^2}{b^2} + \dfrac{c^2}{b^2} = 1$

But $\sin A = \dfrac{a}{b}$ and $\cos A = \dfrac{c}{b}$

Therefore $\sin^2 A + \cos^2 A = 1$

4. By Pythagoras: $a^2 + c^2 = b^2$

Divide both sides by a^2: $\dfrac{a^2 + c^2}{a^2} = \dfrac{b^2}{a^2}$

$\dfrac{a^2}{a^2} + \dfrac{c^2}{a^2} = \dfrac{b^2}{a^2}$

$1 + \dfrac{c^2}{a^2} = \dfrac{b^2}{a^2}$

But $\mathrm{cosec}\, A = \dfrac{b}{a}$ and $\cot A = \dfrac{c}{a}$

Therefore $1 + \cot^2 A = \mathrm{cosec}^2 A$

5. By Pythagoras: $a^2 + c^2 = b^2$

Divide both sides by c^2: $\dfrac{a^2}{c^2} + \dfrac{c^2}{c^2} = \dfrac{b^2}{c^2}$

$\dfrac{a^2}{c^2} + 1 = \dfrac{b^2}{c^2}$

But $\tan A = \dfrac{a}{c}$ and $\sec A = \dfrac{b}{c}$

Therefore $\tan^2 A + 1 = \sec^2 A$

Example

19. Show that the identity $\sin^2 x + \cos^2 x = 1$ is true when $x = 125°$.

Left-hand side $= \sin^2 x + \cos^2 x$
$$= \sin^2 125° + \cos^2 125°$$
$$= 0.8192^2 + (-0.5736)^2$$
$$= 0.6710 + 0.3290$$
$$= 1$$

Right-hand side $= 1$
The identity $\sin^2 x + \cos^2 x = 1$ is true when $x = 125°$.

20. Prove that $\tan A = \dfrac{\sec A}{\operatorname{cosec} A}$

$\text{RHS} = \dfrac{\sec A}{\operatorname{cosec} A}$ but $\operatorname{cosec} A = \dfrac{1}{\sin A}$

$\text{RHS} = \dfrac{\sec A}{\dfrac{1}{\sin A}} = \sec A \sin A$

but $\sec A = \dfrac{1}{\cos A}$

$\text{RHS} = \dfrac{1}{\cos A} \sin A$

$\phantom{\text{RHS}} = \dfrac{\sin A}{\cos A}$

$\phantom{\text{RHS}} = \tan A$

$\text{LHS} = \tan A$

$\text{LHS} = \text{RHS}$

This proves that $\tan A = \dfrac{\sec A}{\operatorname{cosec} A}$

21. Prove that $\sin^2 \theta (\operatorname{cosec}^2 \theta + \sec^2 \theta) = \dfrac{1}{\cos^2 \theta}$

$\text{LHS} = \sin^2 \theta (\operatorname{cosec}^2 \theta + \sec^2 \theta)$

but $\operatorname{cosec} \theta = \dfrac{1}{\sin \theta}$

$\text{LHS} = \sin^2 \theta \left(\dfrac{1}{\sin^2 \theta} + \sec^2 \theta \right)$

but $\sec \theta = \dfrac{1}{\cos \theta}$

$\text{LHS} = \sin^2 \theta \left(\dfrac{1}{\sin^2 \theta} + \dfrac{1}{\cos^2 \theta} \right)$

$\phantom{\text{LHS}} = \dfrac{\sin^2 \theta}{\sin^2 \theta} + \dfrac{\sin^2 \theta}{\cos^2 \theta}$

$\phantom{\text{LHS}} = 1 + \dfrac{\sin^2 \theta}{\cos^2 \theta}$

$\phantom{\text{LHS}} = \dfrac{\cos^2 \theta + \sin^2 \theta}{\cos^2 \theta}$

but $\cos^2 \theta + \sin^2 \theta = 1$

$\text{LHS} = \dfrac{1}{\cos^2 \theta}$

$\text{RHS} = \dfrac{1}{\cos^2 \theta}$

$\text{LHS} = \text{RHS}$

This proves that $\sin^2 \theta (\operatorname{cosec}^2 \theta + \sec^2 \theta)$
$= \dfrac{1}{\cos^2 \theta}$

22. Solve the equation $\sin^2 A - \cos^2 A = ¼$ for angles between 0 and 360°.

Equation: $\sin^2 A - \cos^2 A = ¼$ but $\sin^2 A + \cos^2 A = 1$

so $ (1 - \cos^2 A) - \cos^2 A = ¼$

$ 1 - \cos^2 A - \cos^2 A = ¼$

$ 1 - 2\cos^2 A = ¼$

$ 1 - ¼ = 2\cos^2 A$

$ ¾ = 2\cos^2 A$

so $ \cos^2 A = ⅜$

$ \cos A = \sqrt{⅜}$

$ = \pm 0.6124$

$ A = \cos^{-1} 0.6124$

$ A = 52° 14'$

Since the cosine may be positive or negative there will be one solution in each quadrant, i.e., 52° 14′, 127° 46′, 232° 14′, and 307° 46′.

4.22 Exercises

Without the use of tables or a calculator solve Exercises 1–14.

1. Given that $\sin x = \dfrac{4}{5}$, find $\cos x$ and $\tan x$

2. Given that $\cos x = \dfrac{12}{13}$, find $\sin x$, $\tan x$, $\cosec x$, $\sec x$, and $\cot x$.

3. Given that $\cos A = 0.8$, find $\sin A$ and $\tan A$.

4. Given that $\tan B = \dfrac{12}{5}$ find $\sin B$, $\cos B$, $\sec B$, $\cosec B$, and $\cot B$.

5. Find the value of $\dfrac{\sin A + \cos A}{2 \tan A}$ when $\sin A = 0.6$.

6. Evaluate $\dfrac{\cos 75°}{\sin 15°}$.

7. Find the value of x when $x = \dfrac{\sin 25°}{\cos 65°}$.

8. Show that $\sin 45° + \cos 45° = \dfrac{2}{\sqrt{2}}$

9. Show that $\sin 30° + \cos 60° = 1$

10. Show that $\sin 30° + \cos 60° + \tan 45° = 2$

11. Show that $\cos 30° + \cos 60° = \dfrac{1 + \sqrt{3}}{2}$

12. Show that $\sin 30° - \cos 60° = \dfrac{1 - \sqrt{3}}{2}$

13. Show that $\sin 60° - \cos 30° = 0$

14. Show that $\tan 45° - \sin 45° = \dfrac{\sqrt{2} - 1}{\sqrt{2}}$

Verify the following identities for the angles stated (Exercises 15–19)

15. $\tan x = \dfrac{\sin x}{\cos x}$ for $x = 65°$ and for $x = 165°$.

16. $\sin^2 A + \cos^2 A = 1$ for $x = 78°$ and $x = 187°$.

17. $\sec^2\theta = \tan^2\theta + 1$ for $\theta = 36°$ and $\theta = 240°$.

18. $\cosec^2 B = 1 + \cot^2 B$ for $B = 47°$ and $B = 330°$.

19. $\cot x = \dfrac{\cos x}{\sin x}$ for $x = 60°$ and $x = 170°$.

20. Prove that $\tan x = \sin x \sec x$.

21. Prove that $\cos^2 A = 1 - (\cos A \cdot \tan A)^2$.

22. Prove that $1 + \dfrac{\cos^2 x}{\sin^2 x} = \dfrac{1}{\sin^2 x}$.

23. Prove that $\dfrac{\sec^2 x}{\cosec^2 x} + 1 = \dfrac{1}{\cos^2 x}$.

24. Prove that $\sec^2 A = \sin^2 A \cdot \sec^2 A + 1$.

25. Simplify $\sin^3 x + \sin x \cos^2 x$.

26. Simplify $(\sin A - \cos A)(\sin A + \cos A)$.

27. Simplify $(\sin x + \cos x)^2$.

28. Simplify $\sec x - \sec x \cdot \sin^2 x$.

29. Simplify $\tan A + \dfrac{\cos A}{1 + \sin A}$.

30. Using a right-angled triangle ABC with the right angle at A, derive the relationship $\sin^2 B + \cos^2 B = 1$.

(EMFEC)

31. Using trigonometrical tables only, verify the relationship $\sec^2 \theta = 1 + \tan^2 \theta$ when $\theta = 118°$.

(EMFEC)

32. In a right-angled triangle the sine of angle θ is 0.8. Without using tables or calculators find the value of $\tan \theta$.

(EMFEC)

33. Prove that $1 + \cot^2 A = \cosec^2 A$.

(EMFEC)

34. If $\tan A = \frac{3}{4}$ and A is an acute angle, find, without using a calculator or tables, the values of $\sin 2A$, $\cos 2A$, and $\tan 2A$.

(NWRAC)

35. Copy out the table and complete it, giving your answers in root form:

Angle A	sin A	cos A	tan A
30°			
45°			
60°			

(EMFEC)

36. Find all values of the angle A between 0 and 360° for which $\sec A = -\dfrac{2}{\sqrt{3}}$.

(EMFEC)

37. Prove, without tables or a calculator, that
(a) $\sin 420°\cos 390° - \cos(-300°)\sin(330°) = 1$,
(b) $\cos 210°\sin 150° + \sin 330°\sin 240° = 0$.

(EMFEC)

38. If $\tan A = \dfrac{1}{x}$ find $\sin A$ in terms of x.

(WMAC)

39. Prove that
$$\frac{1}{1 - \sin\theta} - \frac{1}{1 + \sin\theta} = \frac{2\tan\theta}{\cos\theta}.$$

(WMAC)

40. Prove that $\cos^2\theta\tan^2\theta + \dfrac{\sin^2\theta}{\tan^2\theta} = 1$.

(WMAC)

41. Prove the following identity:
$$\frac{\sin\theta\,(\cos\theta - 1)}{1 - \sin^2\theta} = \frac{\sin\theta - \tan\theta}{\cos\theta}$$

(EMFEC)

42. Find the values of θ between 0 and 360° which satisfy the equation
$$\frac{\sin\theta}{\cos\theta} = -\sqrt{3}.$$

(NWRAC)

43. Establish the truth of the following identities:
(a) $2\cos^2 A - 1 = (\cos A + \sin A)(\cos A - \sin A)$;
(b) $(1 - \sin^2 B)\tan^2 B = \sin^2 B$.

(CGLI)

44. If $\sin A = \dfrac{3}{5}$ and $\cos B = \dfrac{5}{13}$, both angles being acute, find without using tables or a calculator, the value of
(a) $2\cos A + 3\tan B$,
(b) $2\sin B + \tan^2 A$.

(YHCFE)

45. Show that $(\cos x + \sin x)^2 + (\cos x - \sin x)^2 = 2$.

(YHCFE)

46. Prove that $\dfrac{2\cos^2 A - 1}{\cos A - \sin A}$
$= \sin A + \cos A$.

(WJEC)

47. Solve the equation $3\cos^2\theta + 2\sin\theta - 2 = 0$, giving all solutions between 0 and 360°.

(WJEC)

48. Find the positive values of θ ($<90°$), which satisfy the equation $3\operatorname{cosec}^2\theta = 10\cot\theta$.

(WMAC)

49. If $t = \tan\frac{1}{2}\theta$ prove that
(a) $\sin\theta = \dfrac{2t}{1 + t^2}$ and
(b) $\cos\theta = \dfrac{1 - t^2}{1 + t^2}$.

(WMAC)

50. If $\tan = 2$, evaluate $\dfrac{\sin A\cos A}{\sin^2 A - \cos^2 A}$ without using tables or a calculator.

(CGLI)

51. Prove that for all values of θ, $\sin^2\theta + \tan^2\theta = \sec^2\theta - \cos^2\theta$.

(CGLI)

4.23 Solid trigonometry with three-dimensional problems

It is necessary, when dealing with problems in three dimensions, to choose and draw suitable triangles in different planes and then to calculate dimensions as required.

A plane is a flat surface, defined as a surface containing all of the straight lines passing through a fixed point and also intersecting a straight line in space.

Examples

23. A component is drawn in Fig. 4.53. Calculate the angle x.

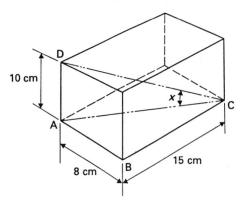

Figure 4.53

From triangle ABC:
$$AC^2 = AB^2 + BC^2$$
$$= 8^2 + 15^2$$
$$= 64 + 225$$
$$= 289$$
$$AC = 17 \text{ cm}$$
From triangle ADC:
$$\tan x = \frac{AD}{AC}$$
$$= \frac{10}{17}$$
$$= 0.5882$$
$$x = \tan^{-1} 0.5882 = 30° 28'$$
The angle x is 30° 28′ and is defined as an angle between a line and a plane.

24. Figure 4.54 shows a large packing case in which AB = 4 m, AD = 3 m, and DH = 5 m.

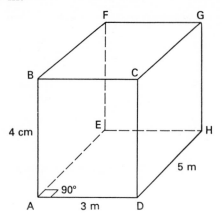

Figure 4.54

Calculate:
(a) the angle between the lines AD and AE;
(b) the angle between the lines AC and AD;
(c) the angle between the lines AD and AF;
(d) the angle between the lines AC and AG;
(e) the angle AC makes with the plane ADEH;
(f) the angle AG makes with the plane ADEH;
(g) the angle AF makes with the plane ADEH;
(h) the angle between the planes ADFG and ADEH;
(i) the angle between the planes ACEG and ADEH.
(j) the angle between the planes ACF and ADEH.

(a) Figure 4.54
     By observation the angle is 90°.
(b) Figure 4.55
$$\tan CAD = \frac{4}{3} = 1.333$$
$$\text{Angle } CAD = 53° 08'$$

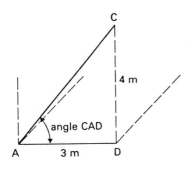

Figure 4.55

$$AC^2 = 3^2 + 4^2 = 9 + 16 = 25$$
$$AC = 5 \text{ m}$$
From the cosine rule:
$$\cos GAC = \frac{7.07^2 + 5^2 - 5^2}{2 \times 7.07 \times 5} = 0.1$$
$$\text{Angle } GAC = 84° \ 16'$$

(e) Figure 4.58
$$\tan CAD = \frac{4}{3} = 1.333$$
$$\text{Angle } CAD = 53° \ 08'$$

(c) Figure 4.56
By observation the angle is 90°.

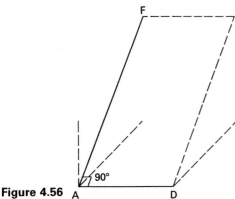

Figure 4.56

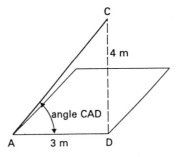

Figure 4.58

(d) Figure 4.57
$$AH^2 = 3^2 + 5^2 = 9 + 25 = 34$$
$$AG^2 = AH^2 + GH^2$$
$$= 5.83^2 + 4^2 = 34 + 16 = 50$$
$$AG \quad 7.07 \text{ m}$$
$$AH = 5.83 \text{ m}$$

(f) Figure 4.59
From part (d) AH = 5.83 m
$$\tan GAH = \frac{4}{5.83} = 0.6861$$
$$\text{Angle } GAH = 34° \ 27'$$

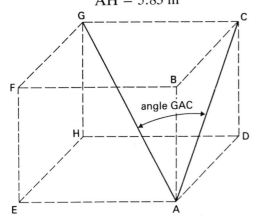

Figure 4.57

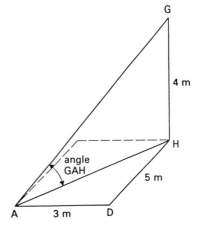

Figure 4.59

(g) Figure 4.60

$$\tan FAE = \frac{4}{5} = 0.8$$

$$\text{Angle } FAE = 38° \ 40'$$

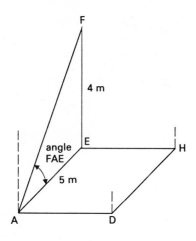

Figure 4.60

(h) Figure 4.61

$$\tan GDH = \frac{4}{5} = 0.8$$

$$\text{Angle } GDH = 38° \ 40'$$

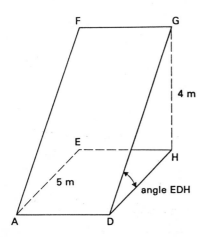

Figure 4.61

(i) Figure 4.62

$$\tan CAD = \frac{4}{3} = 1.333$$

$$\text{Angle } CAD = 53° \ 08'$$

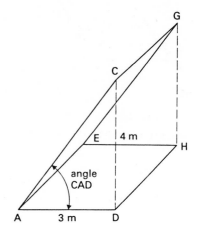

Figure 4.62

(j) Figure 4.63 (a) (b)

$$\text{Length } GH = XY = 4 \text{ m}$$

$$\text{Length } AY = \frac{5.83}{2} = 2.915$$

$$\tan XAY = \frac{4}{2.915} = 1.372$$

$$\text{Angle } XAY = 53° \ 55'$$

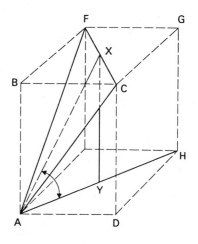

Figure 4.63(a)

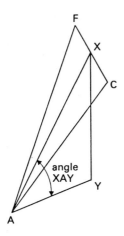

Figure 4.63(b)

Notes:

In items (a) to (d) the calculation has involved an angle between two lines.

In items (e) to (g) the calculation has involved an angle between a line and a plane.

In items (h) to (j) the calculation has involved an angle between two planes.

25. Figure 4.64 represents a pyramid with a square base ABCD of side 3 m. EA = ED = EC = EB = 6 m. Calculate:
    (a) the perpendicular height EF of the pyramid;
    (b) the angle which EA makes with the base;
    (c) the angle which the plane EAD makes with the base.

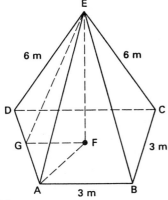

Figure 4.64

(a) From triangle ACB:
$$AC^2 = AB^2 + BC^2 = 3^2 + 3^2 = 18$$
$$AC = 4.243 \text{ m}$$
$$AF = \frac{AC}{2} = \frac{4.243}{2} = 2.1215 \text{ m}$$

From triangle AEF:
$$EF^2 = AE^2 - AF^2 = 6^2 - 2.1215^2$$
$$= 36 - 4.5 = 31.5$$
$$EF = \sqrt{31.5} = 5.613 \text{ m}$$

(b) $\cos EAF = \dfrac{2.1215}{6} = 0.3536$

Angle EAF = 69° 18′

(c) $\tan EGF = \dfrac{5.613}{1.5} = 3.742$

Angle EGF = 75° 02′

26. Two pathways AB and AC meet at the top of a hill at an angle of 90°. The hill is 100 m high. If the pathways make angles of 36 and 47° with the horizontal as shown in Fig. 4.65 determine: (a) the length of each path and (b) the distance between the starting points of the paths.

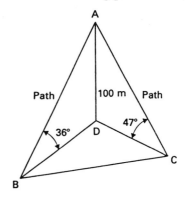

Figure 4.65

Triangle ABD: $\sin 36° = \dfrac{100}{AB}$

$AB = \dfrac{100}{\sin 36°} = 170.1 \text{ m}$

Triangle ACD: $\sin 47° = \dfrac{100}{AC}$

$AC = \dfrac{100}{\sin 47°} = 136.7 \text{ m}$

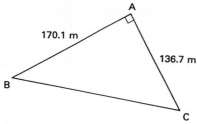

Figure 4.66

Angle A = 90°

$$\tan BCA = \frac{170.1}{136.7} = 1.2443$$

Angle BCA = 51° 13'

$$\cos BCA = \frac{136.7}{BC} \quad BC = \frac{136.7}{\cos 51° 13'}$$

$$= 218.2 \text{ m}$$

The lengths of the paths are 170.1 and 136.7 m with a distance of 218.2 m between the starting points.

4.24 Exercises

1. A component is shown in Fig. 4.67. From the information given calculate (a) angle x, (b) angle y, and (c) angle z.

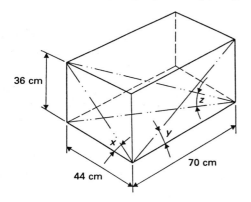

Figure 4.67

2. The component in Fig. 4.68 is a storage container of dimension 3 × 3 × 4 m. Calculate
   (a) the angle between the lines AD and AC,
   (b) the angle between the lines Aa and Ab,
   (c) the angle between the lines AD and Ad,
   (d) the angle between the lines Ad and Ac.

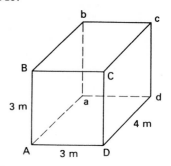

Figure 4.68

3. Figure 4.69 is a square-based pyramid with length OA 4 m. Determine (a) the perpendicular height of the pyramid, (b) the angle OY makes with the pyramid base, (c) the angle which the plane OBC makes with the pyramid base.

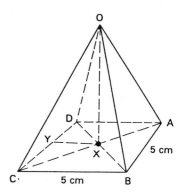

Figure 4.69

4. Figure 4.70 is a wedge. Calculate (a) dimension AC, (b) dimension BC, (c) the angle between the lines DA and DC, (d) the angle between the lines DC and DB, (e) the angle between the lines DB and DE.

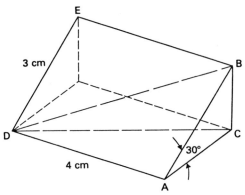

Figure 4.70

5. A solid block of material is 67.5 × 45.8 × 23.6 mm. Determine (a) its longest dimension and (b) the angle the longest dimension makes with the base of the block.

6. A solid pyramid has a square base of side 45 mm with a perpendicular height of 60 mm. Calculate (a) the length of the diagonal of the base, (b) the length of one of the sloping sides, and (c) the angle that the sloping side edge makes with the base.

7. Figure 4.71 shows an inclined plane DE = 2.37 m, AD = 8.5 m, and θ = 22.5°. Find the angle x.

(EMFEC)

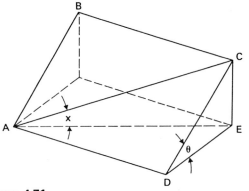

Figure 4.71

8. A rectangular box has dimensions 250 by 300 by 720 mm. Calculate the length of the straight line joining two diagonally opposite corners of the box.

(EMFEC)

9. A rectangular roof 28 by 21 m slopes with the side of length 21 m at an angle of 28° to the horizontal. A water channel runs diagonally across the roof. Determine (a) the length of the water channel and (b) the angle the channel makes with the horizontal.

10. A TV mast is held vertical by a number of cables fastened to its top and pegged to the ground. Two of these wires are inclined at 38° to the vertical, and pegged 50 m from the bottom of the mast. Calculate (a) the length of each cable, (b) the height of the mast, and (c) the distance between the two pegs if the angle between the two cables is 80°.

11. An electrical conduit installation is to be fitted from one floor corner of a workshop to the opposite ceiling corner of the workshop. The conduit is to be fixed to the floor, walls, or ceiling for the whole distance. If the workshop is 12 m long, 6 m wide, and 2.5 m high, draw a diagram showing the conduit path chosen if the shortest route must be taken. Calculate the amount of conduit required and any angles between the conduit and plane faces.

12. A frustum of a right cone is 20 cm diameter at the base and 16 cm diameter at the top. Calculate the length of the sloping side and the angle it makes with the base.

92

Answers

Exercises 4.4

1. (a) 1.326
   (b) 3.299
   (c) 6.021
   (d) 0.790
   (e) 1.116
   (f) 0.796
   (g) 4.480
   (h) 2.509

2. (a) 360°
   (b) 180°
   (c) 135°
   (d) 120°
   (e) 90°
   (f) 45°
   (g) 28° 39′
   (h) 91° 41′
   (i) 154° 43′
   (j) 223° 28′
   (k) 275° 02′

3. 339.3 rad/min

4. 10.47 rad/s

5. (a) 10.91 mm
   (b) 32.73 mm
   (c) 72.87 mm
   (d) 107.8 mm
   (e) 128.3 mm
   (f) 14.5 mm
   (g) 30 mm
   (h) 41.25 mm
   (i) 63.5 mm
   (j) 90.5 mm

6. (a) 1091 mm^2
   (b) 2932 mm^2
   (c) 6000 mm^2
   (d) 7977 mm^2
   (e) 9408 mm^2
   (f) 391 mm^2
   (g) 4883 mm^2
   (h) 7129 mm^2
   (i) 9551 mm^2
   (j) 10742 mm^2

7. 265.8°

8. 45.84°

9. 305.5 mm
   286.8 mm

10. 34.91°
    0.61 rad
    7.82 m

11. 114.6°
    2 rad

12. 1047.3 mm
    375 mm

13. 0.2194 rad/s

14. 251.3 mm

15. 1.114 rev
    20 mm

Exercises 4.6

1. (a) 34.18 mm, 23.31 mm
   (b) 55.31 mm, 13.79 mm
   (c) 87.34 mm, 130.5 mm
   (d) 72.79 mm, 28.44 mm
   (e) 13.95 mm, 29.91 mm
   (f) 20.23 mm, 50.07 mm

2. (a) 27.58°, 62.42°
   (b) 54.12°, 35.88°
   (c) 44.72°, 45.28°
   (d) 28.87°, 61.13°
   (e) 25.20°, 64.80°
   (f) 55.94°, 34.06°

3. 48.9°, 48.9°, 82.2°

4. 20.48°

5. 344.2 mm

6. 116.5 mm

7. 19.29°

8. 349 m

9. 51.71°

10. 6.426 m

11. 548.6 mm
    300 r/min

12. 1450 m

13. 78.49 mm
    119.5 mm
14. 3.64 km
    45° W of N
15. 476
16. 18° 24′
    55 mm
17. 35°
    12.2 m
18. 121.7 m
19. 2.06 m
20. 10° 05′
    34.2 m
21. 8.5 m
    8.7 m
22. 2.8
23. 25 m
    36.87°
    2.5 m
    2 m
24. 109.3 mm
25. 88.85 mm
    18° 40′
    141 mm
    20° 47′
26. 26.1 m
27. 2.728 m
    2.926 m
    4.837 m
28. 69° 31′
    60°
    0.44 m
29. 255°
30. 0.8702
    0.9898
    0.7504
    313.8 m
31. 46 mm
    8.04 mm
    51.91 mm
    120.1 mm
32. 220 m
    190 m
33. 148.3 m
    25°

34. 3.12
    4.16
    2.34
    10.14 cm^2
35. 4.128 mm
    0.4 mm
    91.5 per cent
36. 10.392 m
    6 m
    2.5 m
    2.566 min
37. 229.4
    535.3
    266.8
    809.9 km
    19° 14′
38. 130.8 m
39. 130 m
40. 53.3 m

Exercises 4.12

1. Graph
2. Graph
3. Graph
4. Graph
5. Graph

	6. sine	cosine	tangent
(a)	0.913 545 457	0.406 736 643	2.246 036 774
(b)	0.970 295 726	−0.241 921 895	−4.010 780 934
(c)	−0.965 925 826	0.258 819 045	−3.732 050 808
(d)	−0.819 152 044	0.573 576 436	−1.428 148 007
(e)	0.335 177 522	−0.942 154 991	−0.355 756 245
(f)	−0.818 419 717	−0.575 005 252	1.422 856 077
(g)	−0.248 689 887	0.968 583 161	−0.256 756 360
(h)	0.212 637 211	−0.977 131 217	−0.217 613 773

7. (a) 1
   (b) 0.5
   (c) 0.866 025 403
   (d) 0.707 106 781
   (e) 0.707 106 781
   (f) 0.382 683 432
   (g) 0.923 879 532
   (h) 0.923 879 532
   (i) 0.382 683 432

8.

	sin	cos	tan
(a)	0.0698	−0.9976	−0.0699
(b)	0.9976	−0.0698	−14.300
(c)	−0.1564	−0.9877	0.1584
(d)	−0.9962	−0.0872	11.43
(e)	−0.9877	0.1564	−6.3138
(f)	−0.3420	0.9397	−0.3640

Answers 4.15

1. 72° 42′, 64° 18′, 6.6
2. 32° 48′, 85° 12′, 49.7
3. 37.5, 46.1, 84°
4. 49° 24′, 58° 36′, 218.1
5. 55° 20′, 42° 40′, 165.6
6. 51.9, 47°, 52.7
7. 113.9, 23°, 48.7
8. 86°, 41.3, 77.2
9. 54°, 41.3, 33.8
10. 41°, 34.4, 23.4
11. 36° 49′, 68° 05′
12. 76° 28′, 13° 30′, 90° 02′
13. 27° 50′, 80° 13′, 71° 57′
14. 83.18, 20° 55′, 24° 05′
15. 14.7, 84° 17′, 48° 43′
16. 28° 43′, 65.6, 51° 17′
17. 54° 54′, 89° 06′, 36°
18. 54° 54′, 89° 50′, 35° 16′
19. 22° 59′, 25° 13′, 131° 48′
20. 3.4, 16° 07′, 131° 53′
21. 79.8, 86° 43′, 43° 17′
22. 211.5, 45° 38′, 38° 22′
23. 28° 11′, 121° 49′, 10.59 cm, 45 cm^2
24. 41° 28′
25. 14.16 m, 43° 30′
26. 85.92 mm
27. 196 mm, 63.8 mm
28. 34° 18′, 0.0476 s
29. 518 N
30. 97.2 kN
31. 33.44 m, 35.93 m, 16.75 m
32. 11.21 m, 9.97 m
33. 220 m, 190 m
34. 12°
35. 53° 07′, 6, 8

36. 70 mm, 38° 12′
37. 82° 19′
38. 150 mm, 36° 52′, 29° 55′
39. 6.19 m
40. 2.316 m, 1.879 m
41. 59.8 cm
42. 66.2, 19° 06′
43. 9.52 cm, 23° 23′
44. 67.79 m, 41.87 m

Answers 4.17

1. 12.9, 45° 39′, 77° 41′, 69.2 m^2
2. 58.1, 75° 16′, 39° 44′, 1152 m^2
3. 12.8, 79° 21′, 61° 29′, 81.8 m^2
4. 60.3, 31°, 45°, 683.1 m^2
5. 9.2, 70° 17′, 49° 43′, 34.6 m^2
6. 4.2, 26° 12′, 41° 48′, 27.8 m^2
7. 92° 23′, 81° 37′, 6°, 0.42 m
8. 88° 34′, 88° 46′, 2° 40′, 0.42 m^2
9. 89° 24′, 89° 20′, 1° 16′, 0.44 m^2
10. 70°, 2.7, 4.5, 5.48 m^2
11. 73°, 14.5, 24.1, 166.4 m^2
12. 47°, 12.6, 6.2, 36.12 m^2
13. 47°, 38.8, 28.9, 453.6 m^2
14. 3°, 1.32, 23.6, 14.79 m^2
15. 42°, 100.7, 129, 1899 m^2
16. 39° 25′
17. 3889.6 g
18. 3.464 square units
19. 15.172 cm^2, 0.2216 kg
20. 119.8 mm^2, 70.8 mm^2
21. 350 mm^2
22. 7.46 m, 20° 43′, 9° 48′, 149° 29′
23. 1116.7 m^2
24. 2390 m^2
25. 45 m, 115.8 m

Answers 4.22

1. 0.6
   0.75
2. 5/13
   5/12
   13/5
   13/12
   12/5

3. 0.6
   0.75
4. 12/13
   5/13
   13/5
   13/12
   5/12
5. 14/15
6. 1
7. 1
8–24., Proof
25. $\sin x$
26. $\sin^2 x - \cos^2 x$
27. $1 + 2\sin x \cdot \cos x$
28. $\cos x$
29. sec A
30. Proof
31. Proof
32. 4/3
33. Proof
34. 24/25
    7/25
    24/7
35. ½, $\dfrac{\sqrt{3}}{2}$, $\dfrac{1}{\sqrt{3}}$

    $\dfrac{1}{\sqrt{2}}$ $\dfrac{1}{\sqrt{2}}$, 1

    $\dfrac{\sqrt{3}}{2}$, $\dfrac{1}{2}$, $\sqrt{3}$

36. 150°
    210°
37. Proof
38. $\dfrac{1}{\sqrt{1+x^2}}$
39. Proof
40. Proof
41. Proof
42. 120°
    300°
43. Proof
44. 44/5
    501/208
45. Proof

46. Proof
47. 199° 28′
    340° 32′
    90°
48. 71° 34′
    18° 26′
49. Proof
50. 24/25
    7/25
    24/7
51. Proof

Answers 4.24

1. 39° 17′
   27° 13′
   23° 32′
2. 45°
   36° 52′
   53° 08′
   30° 58′
3. 1.872 m
   36° 49′
   36° 49′
4. 2.6 cm
   1.5 cm
   33° 01′
   17° 27′
   53° 08′
5. 115.4 mm
   16° 08′
6. 63.64 mm
   75 mm
   62° 04′
7. 6° 13′
8. 819.1 mm
9. 35 m
   16° 23′
10. 63.45 m
    39.1 m
    81.57 m
11. 15.92 m
    26° 34′
12. 10.2 cm
    78° 42′

5 Statistics

5.1 Data handling

Statistics is defined as the collection and analysis of data. An introduction to statistics, dealing with tally diagrams, pictograms, bar charts and pie charts, can be found in Chapter 8 of *Mathematics Level 1* of this series.

5.2 Histograms

A histogram is very similar to a vertical bar chart except that a histogram consists of a set of rectangles whose area represents the frequencies under consideration. In a histogram as distinct from a bar chart, it is not necessary for the horizontal intervals to be equal, though they often are.

Examples

1. One question out of six in a test paper have been attempted by 1500 students. Draw a histogram from the table of distribution data.

Question number	1	2	3	4	5	6
Number of students	200	350	150	100	250	450

See Figure 5.1

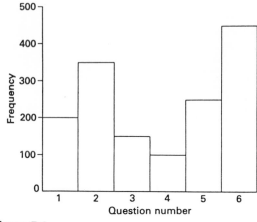

Figure 5.1

2. The marks obtained by 300 students in an examination were as follows:

Marks	10–19	20–29	30–39	40–59	60–79	80–99
Number of students	20	35	40	150	30	25

Draw a histogram of this information.

Points to note:
(a) The width of each set of marks is not the same.
(b) For a histogram we are concerned with the area of the rectangle.
(c) A class width table and a height table need to be constructed.

Marks	10–19	20–29	30–39	40–59	60–79	80–99
Class width	10	10	10	20	20	20
Height of rectangle (Let 1 unit = 10 marks)	$\frac{20}{1}=20$	$\frac{35}{1}=35$	$\frac{40}{1}=40$	$\frac{150}{2}=75$	$\frac{30}{2}=15$	$\frac{25}{2}=12.5$

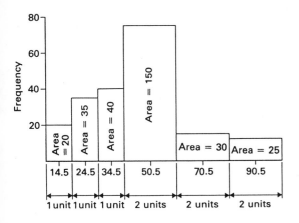

Figure 5.2

5.3 Frequency polygon

When the mid points of the tops of the columns of a histogram are joined together with straight lines we have a frequency polygon.

Example

3. The number of castings per box in a sample of 21 boxes was as follows:

Number in box	70	71	72	73	74	75
Number of boxes	2	6	3	1	4	5

Draw a histogram and a frequency polygon from the information.

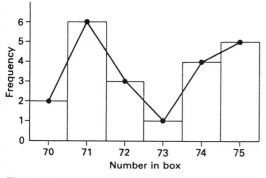

Figure 5.3

5.4 Cumulative frequency

Any frequency distribution can be changed to a cumulative frequency distribution by adding each frequency to the total of its predecessors.

Examples

4. The following table shows the frequency distribution of the marks of 400 students in a test.

Marks	1–20	21–40	41–60	60–80	81–100
Number of students	50	100	150	60	40

Construct a cumulative frequency curve.

Marks	Frequency	Cumulative frequency
Not more than 20	50	50
Not more than 40	100	150
Not more than 60	150	300
Not more than 80	60	360
Not more than 100	40	400

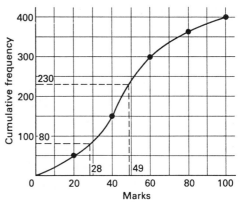

Figure 5.4

The graph of the cumulative frequency shown in Fig. 5.4 is called the cumulative frequency polygon or ogive. The term 'ogive' is used by architects to describe this shape of curves.

5. From Fig. 5.4 answer the following:
   (a) If the pass mark is 50, what percentage of students pass the test?
   (b) If the examinations board decide to allow 80% of the candidates to pass, what should be the pass mark?
   (a) From Fig. 5.4 the number of candidates with not more than 49 marks is 230. Therefore 176 out of 400 fail, i.e., 44%, which means 56% pass.
   (b) From Fig. 5.4 20%, i.e., 80 candidates, have not more than 28 marks. The pass mark should then be 29.

5.5 Exercises

1. The number of entries for an examination per year is given in the table below:

Year	1976	1977	1978	1979	1980	1981	1982	1983
Entries per 1000	17	18	23	29	33	35	43	48

Draw a histogram.

2. Sketch a histogram of the following distribution of x:

Value of x	1	2	3	4	5	6
Frequency	3	7	15	20	13	8

(EMFEC)

3. The lifetime of a component from a production line was tested with a batch of 400 components as shown in the table:

Lifetime (hours)	700–719	720–739	740–759	760–779	780–799	800–819
Frequency	20	45	50	65	120	100

Draw a histogram, a frequency polygon, and a cumulative frequency diagram to represent the information.

4. A machine is set to pack components in boxes of fifty. A random sample test gave the following results:

Number of components packed	44	45	46	47	48	49	50	51	52	53	54	55
Frequency		5	6	7	8	10	12	60	25	45	6	10	15

Draw a histogram, a frequency polygon, and a cumulative frequency diagram from this data.

5. The table below shows the frequency distribution of marks for 800 students at an examination.

Marks	21–30	31–40	41–50	51–60	61–70	71–80	81–90
Frequency	30	50	100	300	130	120	70

Construct a table showing the cumulative frequency distribution and draw a graph of the ogive. If the pass mark is 45, what percentage of students pass the examination.

6. The diameters of 30 components were measured in millimetres with a micrometer, with the following results:

```
5·8   6·2   6·0   6·2   5·9   6·1
5·9   5·7   6·1   5·5   5·8   5·9
6·2   6·1   6·0   6·0   5·9   6·0
6·0   5·9   6·0   6·1   5·9   6·1
6·2   6·3   6·3   6·3   6·3   6·2
```

Construct a table showing a tally diagram; draw a histogram and a frequency polygon; then draw a cumulative frequency diagram.

7. The following table shows the time in minutes taken to complete a turning job for a component on a lathe.
   (a) Produce a frequency table and sort the data into nine suitable groups.
   (b) Draw a histogram of the information and mark on this the values of the class mid-points and boundaries.

```
7.7   8.4   8.1   7.7   7.5   8.2   8.0   7.9   8.5   8.5
8.1   8.2   7.8   8.2   7.9   7.7   7.9   8.3   7.8   7.9
7.6   7.6   8.1   8.0   8.7   8.1   7.3   8.0   7.6   8.4
8.7   8.2   7.5   7.1   7.8   7.6   7.5   7.8   7.9   7.7
7.8   8.1   7.8   8.3   8.1   8.2   8.3   8.3   8.2   7.4
7.9   7.7   7.3   7.6   8.0   7.3   8.1   7.9   7.8   8.1
7.4   7.9   8.0   7.9   7.9   7.8   7.9   7.7   8.0   7.9
8.0   8.1   7.7   8.1   8.1   7.7   7.5   8.0   7.9   7.8
8.2   7.9   8.0   8.0   8.1   8.1   8.1   7.9   8.0   7.9
7.8   7.8   7.8   8.6   8.0   7.3   7.5   7.5   7.8   8.2
```

(EMFEC)

8. The table below shows the thermal conductivity of bricks. Produce a frequency table and sort the data into seven suitable classes.

   Draw a histogram of the information showing clearly the class boundaries and the central point of each class.

0.88	1.14	1.09	1.09	1.15	1.26	1.16
1.02	1.28	1.18	1.34	0.95	1.12	0.94
1.32	1.28	0.96	0.83	0.95	0.83	1.35
0.91	0.98	1.23	1.14	0.77	1.04	1.08
1.18	1.22	1.05	1.39	1.19	1.13	1.09
1.08	1.17	0.80	1.00	1.25	0.82	0.90
0.88	1.01	1.26	1.07	1.04	1.20	1.14
1.04	1.12	1.07	0.84	1.29	0.95	1.05
0.98	1.03	0.72	1.07	1.10	1.23	0.92
1.19	1.02	0.99	1.13	1.05	0.96	1.07

(EMFEC)

5.6 Arithmetic mean, mode and median

Central tendency is a measure of a group of data which allows us to assess the position in which the group stands with respect to other groups of data.

(a) *Arithmetic mean.* The mean is calculated by adding up all of the individual items of data and dividing by the number in the sample.

Example

6. Calculate the mean of three marks obtained by students in a test. The marks are 35, 67, and 48 per cent.

$$\text{Arithmetic mean} = \frac{35 + 48 + 67}{3}$$

$$= \frac{150}{3} = 50\%$$

(b) *Mode.* The mode is the most frequently occurring value in a sample of data. When the frequency distribution of the data is displayed graphically, the mode is the value corresponding to the highest point on the curve.

Example

7. Determine the mode for the set of given values:

   $6, 6, 6, 7, 7, 7, 7, 8, 8, 8, 9, 9, 9, 9, 9, 9, 9.$

   By observation the value 9 occurs with the greatest frequency.

   Mode = 9

(c) *Median.* The median is the point in a set of values that divides the set into two parts containing an equal number of values. When the number of values in the distribution is odd, the median is the middle value. When the number is even, the median is a value midway between the two values nearest the middle.

Examples

8. Calculate the median point for a set of ungrouped data given:

   6, 9, 7, 11, 8, 10 and 6.

   Number of values = 7

   The number of values in the group is *odd*.

   Values arranged in order of magnitude:

   6, 6, 7, ⑧, 9, 10, 11

   Median = 8

9. Calculate the median point for the six given scores from a test paper.

   12, 13, 9, 10, 11, 14.

   Number of scores = 6

   The number of scores in the distribution is *even*.

   Scores arranged in order of magnitude:

   9, 10, | 11, 12, | 13, 14.

   By observation the median lies between 11 and 12.

   $$\text{Median} = \frac{11 + 12}{2} = 11.5$$

10. The diameter of 100 spindles was measured giving the frequency distribution shown in the table:

Diameter (mm)	10	10.2	10.4	10.6	10.8	11.0	11.2
Frequency (number of spindles)	4	8	15	28	32	10	3

Draw a cumulative frequency diagram and from it determine the median.

Diameter not more than	10.1	10.3	10.5	10.7	10.9	11.1	11.3
Frequency	4	8	15	28	32	10	3
Cumulative frequency	4	12	27	55	87	97	100

Because the median is the value that divides the number of spindles into two parts containing an equal number of parts the median can be found from the graph by interpolation, i.e., draw a horizontal line from the cumulative frequency value of $\frac{100}{2} = 50$ and read off the corresponding diameter.

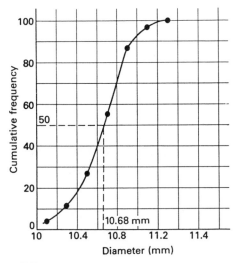

Figure 5.5

From the graph: Median = 10.68 mm.

5.7 Percentiles and quartiles

The percentile rank of a particular value in a given distribution of values, is a number indicating the percentage of values in the whole distribution that fall below the point at which the given value lies.

A quartile is one of three points along the scale of a frequency distribution that divides the distribution into four parts. The first quartile corresponds to the 25th percentile, the second to the median or the 50th percentile, and the third to the 75th percentile.

Example

11. The table below shows the distribution of marks of 400 candidates at an examination.

Marks	1 to 10	11 to 20	21 to 30	31 to 40	41 to 50	51 to 60	61 to 70	71 to 80	81 to 90	91 to 100
Candidates	15	25	50	75	75	65	45	30	15	5

Construct a table showing the cumulative frequency and draw a graph of the ogive and from it determine:
(a) the median mark;
(b) the quartiles;
(c) the percentage number of candidates that pass if the pass mark is 40.

Marks: not more than	10	20	30	40	50	60	70	80	90	100
Frequency	15	25	50	75	75	65	45	30	15	5
Cumulative frequency	15	40	90	165	240	305	350	380	395	400

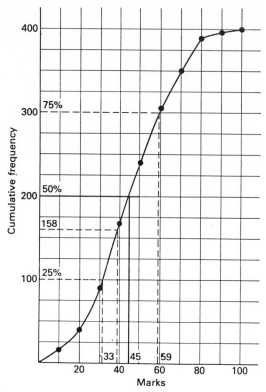

Figure 5.6

By observation from the graph:
(a) Median mark = 45;
(b) Lower quartile = 25th percentile = 33;
Upper quartile = 75th percentile = 59;
(c) The number of candidates with not more than 39 marks is 158. Therefore 158 out of 400 fail but 242 out of 400 pass, i.e., 60.5 per cent pass.

5.8 Exercises

1. The diameters of six bars were measured with a micrometer giving the following results:
16.3 mm, 16.2 mm, 16.1 mm, 16.5 mm, 16.7 mm, 16.4 mm.
Determine the arithmetic-mean diameter.

2. Calculate the arithmetic mean of the following readings:
7 kg, 8 kg, 9 kg, 7.5 kg, 8.5 kg, 9.5 kg, 10 kg, 10.5 kg.

3. A test on ten variable resistors gave the following resistance readings:
25 Ω, 26 Ω, 27 Ω, 28 Ω, 25.2 Ω, 26.4 Ω, 27.8 Ω, 28.5 Ω, 25.3 Ω, 25.1 Ω.
Calculate the arithmetic mean.

4. The times taken in a workshop to repair 40 television sets are recorded in the following table:

Time taken (hours)	1	1.3	1.5	1.6	1.8
Frequency (number of sets)	4	6	8	12	10

Calculate the mean repair time.

5. Determine the mode for the set of given values:
2, 2, 2, 2, 2, 5, 5, 5, 6, 6, 6, 6, 6, 6, 6, 6, 6, 8, 8, 8, 9, 9, 9, 9, 9.

6. Determine the median point for the seven given lengths of carbon steel:
2 m, 2.4 m, 7 m, 6 m, 3.5 m, 8 m, 6.5 m.

7. The current flowing in different parts of a parallel circuit was found to be 1 A, 2.5 A, 2.1 A, 5 A, 6 A, 3.2 A, 6.4 A, 4.5 A, and 5.6 A. Determine the mean and median of electric current.

8. Calculate the median point for the six given test scores: 100 per cent, 90 per cent, 70 per cent, 80 per cent, 60 per cent, 50 per cent.

9. The mass, in kilograms, of 10 castings is shown in the following table:
9.8, 10.2, 10, 9.8, 10.4, 9.6, 9.7, 8.9, 10.1, 9.9.
Determine the mean and median value of mass.

10. The values of mass obtained by weighing 200 components is shown below. Plot a cumulative-frequency curve and find the median and the upper and lower quartiles.

Mass (kg)	93	94	95	96	97	98	99
Frequency	7	30	42	46	40	25	10

(EMFEC)

11. The following table shows the number of goals scored in each match by first division soccer teams in league matches during one season.

Goals in one match	0	1	2	3	4	5	6
Frequency	256	304	194	88	48	24	8

(a) Draw a histogram depicting this information and draw a frequency polygon.
(b) What is the mode of this information?
(c) Draw a cumulative frequency diagram and from it determine the median.

(EMFEC)

12. Plot a cumulative-frequency curve for the data given below, and from it determine the median and the 1st and 3rd quartile values:

Diameter of components (mm)	15.52	15.53	15.54	15.55	15.56	15.57	15.58
Frequency	3	5	8	18	28	16	2

(EMFEC)

13. Tests were carried out on 100 roller-bearings to determine their life expectancy. The results were as follows:

Bearing life per 1000 h	9–12	12–15	15–18	18–21	21–24	24–27	27–30
Frequency	6	9	13	19	26	17	10

Draw a smoothed cumulative-frequency curve (an ogive) and hence determine:
(a) the median life of the roller-bearings,
(b) the first and third quartiles of the distribution.

(EMFEC)

14. The diameter of 100 spindles was measured giving the frequency distribution shown in the table:

Diameter (mm)	10.00 to 10.04	10.05 to 10.09	10.10 to 10.14	10.15 to 10.19	10.20 to 10.24	10.25 to 10.29	10.30 to 10.34
Frequency	4	8	15	28	32	10	3

(a) Draw a frequency-distribution curve for the data and state whether the distribution is skewed to the left or the right.
(b) Draw an ogive and determine the median diameter.

(EMFEC)

15. The approximate distances, in kilometres, travelled to college by the members of a class of twenty students are listed: 15, 5, 10, 20, 5, 5, 15, 15, 20, 15, 5, 5, 10, 10, 15, 10, 5, 10, 25, 5.
(a) Tabulate this data as a frequency table.
(b) Draw a histogram and a cumulative-frequency diagram and state the modal value.

(EMFEC)

16. The table shows the examination marks obtained by 150 candidates in an examination.

Mark (%)	10 to 19	20 to 29	30 to 39	40 to 49	50 to 59	60 to 69	70 to 79	80 to 89	90 to 99
Frequency	3	5	12	35	51	21	12	7	4

Draw a cumulative-frequency distribution (ogive) and from this determine (i) the median, (ii) the number of candidates obtaining a mark less than 65 per cent.

(EMFEC)

17. A sample of 40 concrete cubes were tested to destruction and the following results noted:

Breaking stress (N/mm²)	18	19	20	21	22	23
Number of cubes		2	7	9	14	7	1

(a) Calculate the mean value of stress.
(b) Construct a histogram and a cumulative-frequency diagram, and on it indicate the modal value of stress.
(EMFEC)

18. Forty similar concrete slabs were tested to determine their breaking load (kN), and the results obtained are tabulated:
14, 17, 17, 16, 15, 15, 15, 15, 16, 15, 15, 14, 12, 14, 13, 15, 15, 15, 17, 16, 14, 16, 15, 15, 16, 13, 14, 16, 13, 18, 16, 16, 15, 16, 15, 14, 14, 15, 15, 17.
(a) Tabulate the data in the form of a frequency table.
(b) Draw a histogram and an ogive representing the data.
(c) State the mean and modal value.
(EMFEC)

5.9 Distribution curves

Instead of using a histogram we can show the same data in the form of a distribution curve.

Example

12. Draw a histogram and a distribution curve for the following data:

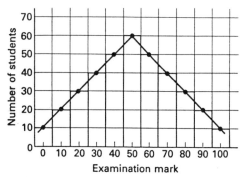

Figure 5.7

The histogram and distribution curve are shown in Fig. 5.7. The distribution curve from the plotted data looks (and indeed is) artificial. A normal distribution curve has the shape shown in Fig. 5.8. Note that the term 'normal' here has a special meaning.

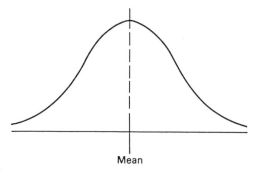

Figure 5.8

In the normal distribution curve and no other the centre point of the horizontal axis is also the mean value. Many shapes of curves are obtained when data is plotted but the types shown in Fig. 5.9 are given special names.

Number of students	10	20	30	40	50	60	50	40	30	20	10
Examination mark	0	10%	20%	30%	40%	50%	60%	70%	80%	90%	100%

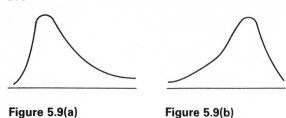

Figure 5.9(a)   **Figure 5.9(b)**

Figure 5.9(a) gives a positively-skewed curve whereas Fig. 5.9(b) gives a negatively-skewed curve.

5.10 Standard deviation

The standard deviation is a measure of variability, dispersion, or spread of data around the mean value of the data. The more closely the data in the distribution clusters around the mean value, the smaller the standard deviation. In a normal distribution 68.2 per cent of all of the data lies within one standard deviation of the mean, as shown in Fig. 5.10.

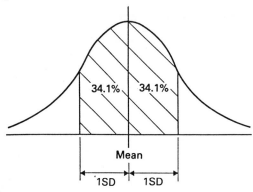

Figure 5.10

Examples

13. Calculate the standard deviation for a set of test scores: 80 per cent, 70 per cent,

65 per cent, 40 per cent, 55 per cent, 50 per cent.

Rules for ungrouped data, i.e., only one of everything:

(a) Calculate the arithmetic mean.
(b) Subtract the mean from the raw data scores.
(c) Square this deviation from the mean.
(d) Add the squared terms.
(e) Calculate the variance by dividing the result from (d) by the number in the sample.
(f) Calculate the standard deviation by taking the square root of the variance.

Arithmetic mean

$$= \frac{80 + 70 + 65 + 40 + 55 + 50}{6}$$

$$= \frac{360}{6} = 60$$

Raw score	Mean	Deviation from mean	Deviation squared
80	60	+20	400
70	60	+10	100
65	60	+ 5	25
40	60	−20	400
55	60	− 5	25
50	60	−10	100
			1050

$$\text{Variance} = \frac{1050}{6} = 175$$

$$\text{Standard deviation} = \sqrt{175} = 13.23$$

14. Calculate the standard deviation for the grouped data given.

Raw score	6	7	8	9	10	11	12	13
Frequency	4	15	16	18	17	19	21	7

Raw score (x)	Frequency (f)	fx	x − mean	(x − mean)²	f(x − mean)²
6	4	24	−3.75	14.0625	56.2500
7	15	105	−2.75	7.5625	113.4375
8	16	128	−1.75	3.0625	49.0000
9	18	162	−0.75	0.5625	10.1250
10	17	170	+0.25	0.0625	1.0625
11	19	209	+1.25	1.5625	29.6875
12	21	252	+2.25	5.0625	106.3125
13	7	91	+3.25	10.5625	73.9375
	117	1141			439.8125

$$\text{Arithmetic mean} = \frac{1141}{117} = 9.75$$

$$\text{Variance} = \frac{439.8125}{117} = 3.7591$$

$$\text{Standard deviation} = \sqrt{3.7591} = 1.94$$

15. Consider the marks awarded to five students for two subjects.

Student	Subject 1 mark	Mean	SD	Subject 2 mark	Mean	SD
A	60	50	10	60	40	15
B	70	50	10	50	40	15
C	50	50	10	70	40	15
D	80	50	10	40	40	15
E	40	50	10	80	40	15

Determine which student should be awarded a class prize.

By observation it will be noted that the arithmetic mean for each student's marks is 50. We cannot therefore use this as a means of awarding the prize.

Consider the standard deviations:

Subject 1

Student A = 60 − 50 = 10, i.e., +1 SD

B = 70 − 50 = 20, i.e., +2 SD

C = 50 − 50 = 0, i.e., 0 SD

D = 80 − 50 = 30, i.e., +3 SD

E = 40 − 50 = −10, i.e., −1 SD

Consider the standard deviations:

Subject 2

Student A = 60 − 40 = 20, i.e., +1⅓ SD

B = 50 − 40 = 10, i.e., + ⅔ SD

C = 70 − 40 = 30, i.e., +2 SD

D = 40 − 40 = 0, i.e., 0 SD

E = 80 − 40 = 40, i.e., +2⅔ SD

For each student a total standard deviation can now be calculated:

Student A = +1 + 1⅓ = +2⅓ SD

B = +2 + ⅔ = +2⅔ SD

C = 0 + 2 = +2 SD

D = +3 + 0 = +3 SD*

E = −1 + 2⅔ = +1⅔ SD

By observation, student D has the highest standard deviation and would be awarded the prize. This information can be seen represented in Fig. 5.11.

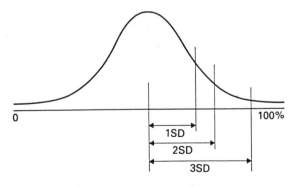

Figure 5.11 Three standard deviations being nearest to the maximum available.

5.11 Exercises

1. Sketch the following distribution curves:
   (a) Normal distribution,
   (b) Distribution with a positive skew,
   (c) Distribution with a negative skew.

2. Calculate the arithmetic mean and the standard deviation for the given set of numbers:
   6, 7, 8, 9, 10, 11, 12, 13, 14, 15.

3. The electrical energy consumption for a domestic dwelling over four quarters was 1689 kWh, 1436 kWh, 1504 kWh, and 1796 kWh. Determine the mean and standard deviation of energy consumed.

4. The following table gives recurring values of x:

Value of x	0	1	2	3	4	5
Frequency (f)	13	25	32	18	7	5

Calculate the mean and standard deviation.

(EMFEC)

5. The following table gives recurring values of x:

Value of x	4	5	6	7	8
Frequency (f)	9	14	52	18	7

Calculate the mean value of x and the standard deviation.

(EMFEC)

6. The frequency of recurring values of variable x is given by the histogram shown in Fig. 5.12.

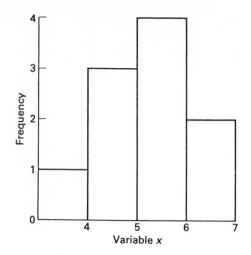

Figure 5.12

Calculate the mean value and standard deviation of variable x.

(EMFEC)

7. The lengths of 80 components were measured and the mean length was calculated to be 12.46 cm with a standard deviation of 0.02 cm. How many components would be expected to have a length between 12.42 and 12.5 cm if the lengths formed a normal distribution?

(EMFEC)

8. Using electronic equipment, a land surveyor made the following measurements, in metres, of the distance between two fixed marks:
   100.123, 100.122, 100.122, 100.124,
   100.120, 100.121, 100.124, 100.125,
   100.124, 100.119, 100.118, 100.122.
   Determine the mean value of these observations and calculate the standard deviation.

(EMFEC)

9. The following table shows the number of hours worked by 100 employees in a certain week:

Hours per man	39	40	41	42	43	44	45
Number of men	5	9	13	18	23	20	12

Calculate the mean and standard deviation of the number of hours worked per man.

(EMFEC)

10. (a) Sketch a normal distribution curve.
    (b) State the percentage area under the normal curve bounded by (i) one standard deviation on either side of mean, (ii) two standard deviations on either side of mean.

(EMFEC)

11. Draw a frequency curve for the table of values below which were obtained from 100 tensile tests on low carbon steel specimens.

Maximum load (kN)	50	55	60	65	70	75	80
Frequency		1	4	15	28	36	14	2

State whether the curve is symmetric, right-hand skewed, or left-hand skewed.

(EMFEC)

12. Quality control tests showed that the mean diameter of pins produced on an automatic lathe was 16.4 mm and the standard deviation was 0.2 mm. If the diameters form a normal distribution, how many pins in a batch of 1000 could be expected to be (i) less than 16.2 mm diameter, (ii) over 16.8 mm diameter?

(EMFEC)

13. A random sample of items was extracted from a production line, measured on dimensions nominally 6 ± 0.5 units, and put into categories as follows:

Variate (x)	5.6	5.8	6.0	6.2	6.4
Frequency (f)	2	8	19	15	6

(a) Calculate the arithmetic mean and standard deviation x.
(b) If this sample is representative of large-scale production explain why the production of defective articles outside the limits is unavoidable.

(CGLI)

14. A random sample of 50 castings obtained from a die-casting machine were weighed and allocated categories. The resulting distribution was symmetrical, as follows:

Mass (kg)	5.0	5.1	5.2	5.3	5.4
Frequency	6	12	14	12	6

(a) State the mean, and establish the standard deviation of the mass.
(b) If this sample can be considered to be representative of large scale production, determine (i) the approximate maximum and minimum mass of the castings produced in quantities (ii) the percentage of castings that can be expected to have a mass over 5.14 kg.

Use the following approximate areas under the curve of normal distribution.

Units of SD	±0.5	±1	±1.5	±2	±2.5	±3.1
Percentage	38	68	79	95	99	100

(CGLI)

110

Answers

Exercises 5.5

1–8. Diagrams

Exercises 5.8

1. 16.37 mm
2. 8.75 kg
3. 26.43 Ω
4. 1.525 h
5. 6
6. 6
7. 4.03 A
   3.2 A
8. 75 per cent
9. 9.84 kg
   9.85 kg
10. 95.4 kg
    94.3 kg
    96.6 kg
11. 1
    0.9
12. 15.553 mm
    15.543 mm
    15.558 mm
13. 21.5 h
    17 h
    24.5 h
14. Right
    10.18 mm
15. 5
16. 54 per cent
    110
17. 21 N/mm^2
18. 17.15 kN
    15 kN

Exercises 5.11

1. Sketches
2. 10.5
   2.87
3. 1606.25
   143.4
4. 1.96
   1.296
5. 6
   0.9798
6. 250
   119
7. 76
8. 100.122
   0.00204
9. 42.52
   1.666
10. Sketch
    68.2 per cent
    95.44 per cent
11. Right
12. 330
    23
13. 6.06
    0.201
    6 $\pm$ 0.5 is inside mean $\pm$ 3 SD
14. 5.2 kg
    0.12 kg
    5.572 kg
    4.828 kg
    69 per cent

6 Boolean Algebra

Boolean algebra is a branch of symbolic logic, named after George Boole (1815–64), which is used in electronics to perform operations using a two-state condition.

6.1 Two-state devices

When you walk into a dark room and operate the light switch you are using a two-state device. The switch is either ON or OFF. When it is off you are using 0 volts and when it is ON you are using 240 volts to supply a lamp. To simplify matters we can say that we are in a '0' or '1' situation.

6.2 The OR operator

The addition sign + in ordinary algebra is used to represent the OR operation in Boolean algebra. We can have the following conditions:
$0 + 0 = 0, 0 + 1 = 1, 1 + 0 = 1, 1 + 1 = 1.$

Note carefully the last of these conditions.

6.3 The AND operator

The multiplication sign from ordinary algebra is used to represent the AND operator in Boolean algebra. We can have the following conditions:
$0 \times 0 = 0, 0 \times 1 = 0, 1 \times 0 = 0, 1 \times 1 = 1.$
Again note carefully the last of these conditions.

6.4 The NOR operator

The NOR operator is always opposite to that of the OR operator.

6.5 Types of logic gates

A logic gate is the name given to a circuit which may have more than one input but one output. The input and output signals are always in a '0' or '1' state called binary signals. For convenience binary inputs to any gate will be labelled A, B, or C, etc., and the output from the gate as F. The British Standard graphical symbols for the various binary logic gates are shown in Fig. 6.1.

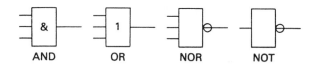

Figure 6.1

6.6 Truth tables

With a number of inputs per gate, the input–output relationship can be expressed in the form of a truth table. A truth table lists all the possible combinations from differing input arrangements. The number of combinations can be found by using the formula:

Number of input combinations = 2^x

where x = number of inputs A, B, etc.

111

Examples

1. Determine the number of inputs available for (a) a 2-input gate and (b) a 3-input gate. List the inputs for each situation.

   (a) $x = 2$

   Number of input combinations =
   $2^x = 2^2 = 4$

   Inputs:

A	B
0	0
0	1
1	0
1	1

   (b) $x = 3$

   Number of input combinations =
   $2^x = 2^3 = 8$

   Inputs:

A	B	C
0	0	0
0	0	1
0	1	0
0	1	1
1	0	0
1	0	1
1	1	0
1	1	1

   To complete a truth table showing the outputs available we use the rules given in Secs. 6.2 and 6.3.

2. Given a two-input OR gate draw up a table showing the outputs. $x = 2$.
   Number of input combinations = $2^x = 2^2 = 4$
   OR gate rule: Use the + sign from algebra.

   Table:

Inputs		Output
A	B	F
0	0	0
0	1	1
1	0	1
1	1	1

   N.B. The output will stand at its defined 1-state if, and only if, one or more of its inputs stand at their defined 1-states.

3. Given a two-input AND gate draw up a table showing the outputs. $x = 2$
   Number of input combinations = $2^x = 2^2 = 4$
   AND gate rule: Use the $\times$ sign from algebra.

   Table:

Inputs		Output
A	B	F
0	0	0
0	1	0
1	0	0
1	1	1

   N.B. The output will stand on its defined 1-state if, and only if, ALL of the inputs stand at their defined 1-state.

4. Given a two-input NOR gate draw up a table showing the outputs. $x = 2$
   Number of input combinations = $2^x = 2^2 = 4$
   NOR gate rule: Use the OR gate rule and then the NOR gate will be the opposite of the OR gate output.

   Table:

Inputs		Output	Output
A	B	OR gate	NOR gate
0	0	0	1
0	1	1	0
1	0	1	0
1	1	1	0

5. Complete the truth table for a three-input AND, OR, and NOR gate. $x = 3$
   Number of input combinations = $2^x = 2^3 = 8$

Table:

Inputs			Output	Output	Output
A	B	C	AND gate	OR gate	NOR gate
0	0	0	0	0	1
0	0	1	0	1	0
0	1	0	0	1	0
0	1	1	0	1	0
1	0	0	0	1	0
1	0	1	0	1	0
1	1	0	0	1	0
1	1	1	1	1	0

6.7 Logic function notation

Completing long truth tables can become a very tedious business, so we use an algebraic system. Consider the example of one input A and one output F. If we assume the output signal to be the same as the input signal, the truth table would be as follows:

Input	Output
A	F
0	0
1	1

This result can be expressed as $F = A$

Consider the next example to give an output as shown in the truth table:

Input	Output
A	F
0	1
1	0

In this case the output value is opposite to that of the input and can be expressed as $F =$ not A, or written as $F = \bar{A}$, where the bar symbol is used for the NOT situation. This is often referred to as an inverter gate, i.e., $F = \bar{A}$, so that $\bar{0} = 1$ and $\bar{1} = 0$.

Following this convention for an AND gate with two inputs we can write $F = AB$ or $F = A{\cdot}B$. Likewise for the OR gate we can write $F = A + B$.

Examples

6. Complete the following truth table for ten different output functions.

Inputs		Outputs F									
A	B	AB	$\overline{AB}$	$A\bar{B}$	$\bar{A}B$	$\bar{A}.\bar{B}$	$A+B$	$\overline{A+B}$	$\bar{A}+B$	$A+\bar{B}$	$\bar{A}+\bar{B}$
0	0	0	1	0	0	1	0	1	1	1	1
0	1	0	1	0	1	0	1	0	1	0	1
1	0	0	1	1	0	0	1	0	0	1	1
1	1	1	0	0	0	0	1	0	1	1	0

7. Express the input–output relationship for a three-input OR gate with inputs A, B, and C.

    From Sec. 6.7

Let F = output, then

$F = A + B + C$

8. Express the input–output relationship for a three-input AND gate with inputs A, B, and C.

    From Sec. 6.7

Let F = output then

$F = ABC$

9. Express the input–output relationship for a three-input NOR gate with inputs A, B, and C.

    From Sec. 6.7

Let F = output then

$F = \overline{A + B + C}$

10. Write down a Boolean expression for the input–output relationship of the following truth table:

Input		Output
A	B	F
0	0	0
0	1	0
1	0	1
1	1	0

By observation we can check that it does not follow the form $F = AB$ because of the third input and also it does not follow the form $F = A + B$ because of the fourth input.

The correct output can then only be found by using $\bar{A}$ or $\bar{B}$ in the most appropriate combination to give the output required.

Test case 1. Try $\bar{A}$ with B

Truth table:

Input		Output	Output
$\bar{A}$	B	$\bar{A}+B$	$\bar{A}B$
1	0	1	0
1	1	1	1
0	0	0	0
0	1	1	0

This combination does not give the required output.

Test case 2. Try A with $\bar{B}$

Truth table:

Input		Output	Output
A	$\bar{B}$	$A+\bar{B}$	$A\bar{B}$
0	1	1	0
0	0	0	0
1	1	1	1
1	0	1	0

We can note that the output $A\bar{B}$ gives the required Boolean expression.
Therefore $F = A\bar{B}$.

11. Draw a logic circuit diagram for the expression $F = \bar{A}B$.

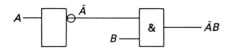

Figure 6.2

12. Design a logic circuit to give the output $\bar{A}BCD\bar{E}$.

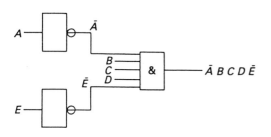

Figure 6.3

13. Design a logic circuit whose output is $\bar{A} + \bar{B} + \bar{C}$ using inputs A, $\bar{B}$, and $\bar{C}$.

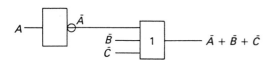

Figure 6.4

6.8 Exercises

1. Draw the British Standard graphical symbols for the following gates (a) OR, (b) AND, (c) NOR, (d) NOT.

2. Compile a truth table for a two-input and a three-input OR gate.

3. Calculate the number of input combinations that are available for a two-input and a three-input gate.

4. Compile a truth table for a three-input OR and NOR gate.

5. Given a two-input and a three-input AND gate, draw up truth tables showing the outputs that are available.

6. Complete a truth table for a four-input AND, OR, and NOR gate.

7. Express the input–output relationship for a two-input (a) OR gate, (b) AND gate, and (c) NOR gate.

8. Given four inputs A, B, C, and D state the output for (a) an AND gate, (b) an OR gate, and (c) a NOR gate.

9. Write down a Boolean expression for the various outputs shown in the following truth table:

Input A	B	Output F1	Output F2	Output F3	Output F4	Output F5	Output F6
0	0	0	0	0	0	1	1
0	1	0	1	1	0	1	0
1	0	0	1	0	1	0	1
1	1	1	1	0	0	1	1

10. Draw a logic circuit diagram for the following expressions:
    (a) $F = A\bar{B}$; (b) $F = \bar{A}B$;
    (c) $F = A + \bar{B}$; (d) $F = \bar{A} + B$;
    (e) $F = \bar{A}BC$; (f) $F = A\bar{B}C$;
    (g) $F = AB\bar{C}$; (h) $F = \bar{A}B\bar{C}$.

11. Design a logic circuit to give the following outputs:
    (a) $\bar{A}BCD$; (b) $A\bar{B}CD$; (c) $AB\bar{C}D$;
    (d) $\bar{A}B\bar{C}D$; (f) $A\bar{B}C\bar{D}$.

12. State the relationship for the input–output of an AND gate with five inputs A, B, C, D, and E.

13. Write down the input–output relationship of a four-input OR gate with inputs A, B, C and D.

14. State the input–output relationship of a three-input NOR gate with inputs A, B, and C.

15. Determine the input–output relationship for the following truth table:

Inputs A	B	Output F
0	0	0
0	1	1
1	0	1
1	1	0

16. Complete the following truth table for the different output functions:

17. Write down the Boolean expression for the logic system given by the following truth table:

Inputs A	B	C	Output F
0	0	0	0
0	0	1	0
0	1	0	1
0	1	1	0
1	0	0	0
1	0	1	1
1	1	0	0
1	1	1	0

18. Sketch the circuit diagram using OR, NOT, and AND gates for the situation in Exercise 17.

19. What is the output F when $A = 1$, $B = 1$, and $C = 0$ in the circuit in Fig. 6.5

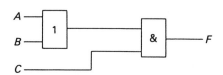

Figure 6.5

20. Determine the output F for the combination of gates in the circuit in Fig. 6.6 when (a) $A = 1$, $B = 1$, and $C = 1$; (b) $A = 1$, $B = 0$, and $C = 1$; and (c) $A = 1$, $B = 1$, and C = 0.

Inputs A	B	C	ABC	$\overline{AB}C$	$\overline{A}\overline{B}C$	$A\overline{B}C$	$A + B + C$	$\overline{A + B + C}$	$\bar{A} + B + C$	$\bar{A} + \bar{B} + C$
0	0	0								
0	0	1								
0	1	0								
0	1	1								
1	0	0								
1	0	1								
1	1	0								
1	1	1								

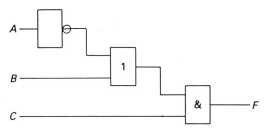

Figure 6.6

Answers

Exercises 6.8

1. See Fig. 6.1

2.

Input		Output
A	B	F
0	0	0
0	1	1
1	0	1
1	1	1

Input			Output
A	B	C	F
0	0	0	0
0	0	1	1
0	1	0	1
0	1	1	1
1	0	0	1
1	0	1	1
1	1	0	1
1	1	1	1

3. 4
   8

4.

Input			Output OR	Output NOR
A	B	C		
0	0	0	0	1
0	0	1	1	0
0	1	0	1	0
0	1	1	1	0
1	0	0	1	0
1	0	1	1	0
1	1	0	1	0
1	1	1	1	0

5.

Input		Output AND
A	B	
0	0	0
0	1	0
1	0	0
1	1	1

Input			Output AND
A	B	C	
0	0	0	0
0	0	1	0
0	1	0	0
0	1	1	0
1	0	0	0
1	0	1	0
1	1	0	0
1	1	1	1

6.

Input				Output AND	Output OR	Output NOR
A	B	C	D			
0	0	0	0	0	0	1
0	0	0	1	0	1	0
0	0	1	0	0	1	0
0	0	1	1	0	1	0
0	1	1	1	0	1	0
0	1	0	1	0	1	0
0	1	1	0	0	1	0
0	1	1	1	0	1	0
1	0	0	0	0	1	0
1	0	0	1	0	1	0
1	0	1	0	0	1	0
1	0	1	1	0	1	0
1	1	0	0	0	1	0
1	1	0	1	0	1	0
1	1	1	0	0	1	0
1	1	1	1	1	1	0

7. $F = A + B$
   $F = AB$
   $F = \overline{A + B}$

8. $F = ABCD$
   $F = A + B + C + D$
   $F = \overline{A + B + C + D}$

9. $F1 = AB$
   $F2 = A + B$
   $F3 = \bar{A}B$
   $F4 = A\bar{B}$
   $F5 = \bar{A} + B$
   $F6 = A + \bar{B}$

10. Diagram
11. Diagram
12. $F = ABCDE$
13. $F = A + B + C + D$
14. $F = \overline{A + B + C}$
15. $F = \bar{A}B + A\bar{B}$

16.

Input			ABC	$\overline{ABC}$	$\overline{AB}C$	$A\overline{BC}$	$A + B + C$	$\overline{A + B + C}$	$\bar{A} + B + C$	$\bar{A} + \bar{B} + C$
A	B	C								
0	0	0	0	1	0	0	0	1	1	1
0	0	1	0	1	1	0	1	0	1	1
0	1	0	0	1	0	0	1	0	1	1
0	1	1	0	1	0	0	1	0	1	1
1	0	0	0	1	0	1	1	0	0	1
1	0	1	0	1	0	0	1	0	1	1
1	1	0	0	1	0	0	1	0	1	0
1	1	1	1	0	0	0	1	0	1	1

17. $F = \bar{A}B\bar{C} + A\bar{B}C$
18. Diagram
19. $F = (A + B)C$
20. 1
    0
    0

7 Differential Calculus

The study of problems associated with tangents to curves led to the invention of differential and integral calculus by Isaac Newton (1642–1727) and Gottfried Wilhelm Leibniz (1646–1716). All calculus is now based on the concepts of *function* and *limit*.

7.1 Gradient of a curve: graphical method

From the equation $y = x^2$ we can compile a table of results for values of x from -4 to $+4$ and draw a graph as shown in Fig. 7.1.

x	-4	-3	-2	-1	0	1	2	3	4
y	16	9	4	1	0	1	4	9	16

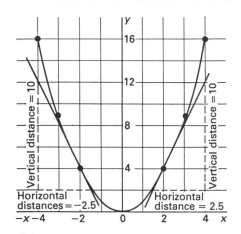

Figure 7.1

By observation: As the value of x increases so does the value of y, but the values of y are increasing at different rates to that of x. By determining the gradient of a curve at a particular point we can then state the rate of change of y with respect to x.

Examples

1. Find the gradient of the curve $y = x^2$ at the point where $x = +2.5$.
   From the graph:
   Vertical distance = 10
   Horizontal distance = 2.5
   From Sec. 2.2:
   $$\text{Gradient} = \frac{\text{vertical distance}}{\text{horizontal distance}}$$
   $$= \frac{10}{2.5}$$
   $$= 4$$
   The gradient of the curve $y = x^2$ is 4 at the point $x = 2.5$.

2. Find the gradient of the curve $y = x^2$ at the point where $x = -2.5$.
   From the graph:
   Vertical distance = 10
   Horizontal distance = -2.5
   From Sec. 2.2:
   $$\text{Gradient} = \frac{\text{vertical distance}}{\text{horizontal distance}}$$
   $$= \frac{10}{-2.5}$$
   $$= -4$$
   The gradient is a negative value because the tangent of the curve is sloping downwards from left to right.
   The gradient of the curve $y = x^2$ is -4 at the point $x = -2.5$.

7.2 Exercises

Find the gradients of the following curves at the point of x, given:
1. $y = 2x^2$ at $x = 3$
2. $y = 2x^2$ at $x = -3$

120

3. $y = x^2 + x$ at $x = 2$
4. $y = x^2 + x + 2$ at $x = 2$
5. $y = 2x^2 + x = 4$
6. $y = 3x^2$ at $x = 4$
7. $y = 3x^2$ at $x = -3$
8. $y = 3x^2 + 2x$ at $z = -2$
9. $y = 2x^2 + 3x + 2$ at $x = -3$ and $x = +3$
10. $y = 3x^2 + 4x$ at $x = 4$
11. $y = 2x^2 - 2x$ at $x = -1$ and $x = 2$
12. $y = 3x^2 - 3x$ at $x = 2$ and $x = 4$
13. $y = 2x^2 + 2x + 2$ at $x = -3$ and $x = +3$
14. $y = 3x^2 - 2x - 4$ at $x = -1$ and $x = +2$
15. $y = x^3$ at $x = -2$ and $x = +2$
16. $y = 3x^3$ at $x = 4$
17. $y = x^3 + 2x$ at $x = -2$ and $x = +2$
18. $y = 2x^3 + 4x$ at $x = -3$ and $x = +4$
19. $y = 2x^3 + 5x + 6$ at $x = -5$ and $x = +5$
20. $y = 4x^3 - 5x - 1$ at $x = 4$

7.3 Gradient of a curve: numerical method

Drawing a graph and determining the gradient from the graph can be a fairly lengthy and often tedious business, so a numerical method has been evolved.

For a small increase in x we can write δx, δ being the lower-case for a Greek letter d (delta). In a like manner δy means a small increase in y. Consider Fig. 7.2:
At co-ordinate (5, 25) we have $\delta x = 2$ and $\delta y = 16$ so $\dfrac{\delta y}{\delta x} = \dfrac{16}{2} = 8.$

The table shows how $\dfrac{\delta y}{\delta x}$ changes as A moves nearer to B.

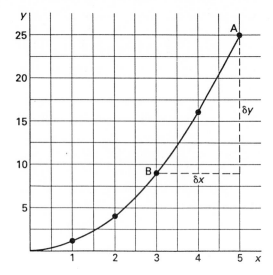

Figure 7.2

From the table we observe that as δx decreases, $\dfrac{\delta y}{\delta x}$ decreases, and by making x small enough, we can ensure that $\dfrac{\delta y}{\delta x}$ is very close to 6. The limiting value of $\dfrac{\delta y}{\delta x}$ is approaching 6 as x approaches 0. Therefore

$$\underset{x \to 0}{\text{Limit}} \frac{\delta y}{\delta x} = \frac{dy}{dx} = 6$$

This can now be confirmed mathematically:
Equation: $y = x^2$
When y changes by a small amount it becomes $y + \delta y$ so a change in x becomes $x + \delta x$.
By substitution into $y = x^2$ we have
$$y + \delta y = (x + \delta x)^2$$
$$y + \delta y = (x + \delta x)(x + \delta x)$$
$$y + \delta y = x^2 + 2x\,\delta x + \delta x^2$$
But $y = x^2$ so $\delta y = 2x\,\delta x + \delta x^2$
Divide both sides by δx
$$\frac{\delta y}{\delta x} = \frac{2x\,\delta x + \delta x^2}{\delta x}$$
$$\frac{\delta y}{\delta x} = 2x + \delta x$$

As A approaches B, in Fig. 7.2, δx decreases indefinitely and $\dfrac{y}{\delta x}$ tends, in the limit, to the

x	y	δy	δx	Gradient $= \dfrac{\delta y}{\delta x}$
5.0	25.00	16.00	2.0	8.0
4.5	20.25	11.25	1.5	7.5
4.0	16.00	7.00	1.0	7.0
3.5	12.25	3.25	0.5	6.5
3.1	9.61	0.61	0.1	6.1
3.01	9.0601	0.0601	0.01	6.01

gradient of the curve at point B. We call this limiting value $\dfrac{dy}{dx}$. Therefore $\underset{x \to 0}{\text{Limit}} \dfrac{\delta y}{\delta x} = \dfrac{dy}{dx}$

$= 2x$

From Fig. 7.2, at point B, $x = 3$,

then $\dfrac{dy}{dx} = 2x = 2 \times 3 = 6$.

The process of determining $\dfrac{dy}{dx}$ is

entiation, and $\dfrac{dy}{dx}$ is called the derivative of y.

Examples

3. Find from first principles the differential coefficient of x^3 with respect to x.

Equation: $y = x^3$

Let δx be a small change in x and δy be the corresponding change in y, then

$y + \delta y = (x + \delta x)^3$

$\qquad = (x + \delta x)(x + \delta x)(x + \delta x)$

$\qquad = (x + \delta x)(x^2 + 2x\,\delta x + \delta x^2)$

$\qquad = x^3 + 2x^2\,\delta x + x\,\delta x^2 + x^2$
$\qquad\quad \delta x + 2x\,\delta x^2 + \delta x^3$
$\qquad = x^3 + 3x^2\,\delta x + 3x\,\delta x^2 + \delta x^3$

But $y = x^3$ so

$\delta y = 3x^2\,\delta x + 3x\,\delta x^2 + \delta x^3$

$\therefore \dfrac{\delta y}{\delta x} = 3x^2 + 3x\,\delta x + \delta x^2$

The differential coefficient:

$\dfrac{dy}{dx} = \underset{\delta x \to 0}{\text{Limit}} \dfrac{\delta y}{\delta x}$

$\qquad = \underset{\delta x \to 0}{\text{limit}} \,(3x^2 + 3x\,\delta x + \delta x^2)$

$\dfrac{dy}{dx} = 3x^2$

4. Differentiate from first principles $y = x^2 + 4x$ and find the value of the gradient of the curve at $x = 3$.

Equation: $y = x^2 + 4x$

Let δx be a small change in x and δy be the corresponding change in y, then

$y + \delta y = (x + \delta x)^2 + 4\,(x + \delta x)$

$y + \delta y = x^2 + 2x\,\delta x + \delta x^2 + 4x + 4\delta x$

But $y = x^2 + 4x$ so

$\delta y = 2x\,\delta x + \delta x^2 + 4\delta x$

$\therefore \dfrac{\delta y}{\delta x} = 2x + \delta x + 4$

The differential coefficient:

$\dfrac{dy}{dx} = \underset{\delta x \to 0}{\text{Limit}} \dfrac{\delta y}{\delta x}$

$\qquad = \underset{\delta \to 0}{\text{limit}} \,(2x + \delta x + 4)$

$\dfrac{dy}{dx} = 2x + 4$

When $x = 3$ $\dfrac{dy}{dx} = (2 \times 3) + 4 = 6 + 4$

$\qquad\qquad = 10$

The gradient of the curve at $x = 3$ is 10.

7.4 Exercises

Differentiate the following from first principles:

1. $y = 2x^2$
2. $y = 2x^3$
3. $y = x^2 + 2$
4. $y = x^3 + 3$
5. $y = x^2 + 2x$
6. $y = x^3 + 3x$
7. $y = x^2 + 3x + 2$
8. $y = x^3 + 2x + 1$
9. $y = x^2 - 2x$
10. $y = x^3 + x - 4$
11. $y = 3x + 2$
12. $s = 4t^2 - 3t + 2$
13. $A = \pi r^2$
14. $y = \dfrac{1}{x}$
15. $y = 1 + 2x^2$
16. $y = x^2 - 3x + 2$

(EMFEC)

7.5 Differentiation

Determining the gradient of a curve y being a function of x is called differentiating y with respect to x. As shown the gradient is represented by the symbol $\dfrac{dy}{dx}$. Sometimes the general equation is written $y = f(x)$ and $\dfrac{dy}{dx}$ is written $f'(x)$. Both $\dfrac{dy}{dx}$ and $f'(x)$ are termed the derived functions or derivatives. To avoid the lengthy process used in Sec. 7.3 a rule can be applied:

If $y = ax^n$ then $\dfrac{dy}{dx} = anx^{(n-1)}$

Examples

5. Differentiate with respect to x the following:
   (a) $y = x^2$; (b) $y = 4x^3$; (c) $y = 3x^2 + 5$;
   (d) $y = 4x^2 + 3x + 6$; (e) $y = \dfrac{1}{x}$.

   (a) Equation $y = x^2$

   Rule: When $y = ax^n$ then$\dfrac{dy}{dx} = anx^{(n-1)}$

   Therefore
   $\dfrac{dy}{dx} = 2x^{(2-1)} = 2x^1 = 2x$

   (b) Equation: $y = 4x^3$
   $\dfrac{dy}{dx} = (3 \times 4)\, x^{(3-1)} = 12x^2$

   (c) Equation: $y = 3x^2 + 5$
   $\dfrac{dy}{dx} = (2 \times 3)\, x^{(2-1)} = 6x$

   (d) Equation: $y = 4x^2 + 3x + 6$
   $\dfrac{dy}{dx} = (2 \times 4)x^{(2-1)} + (1 \times 3)x^{(1-1)} + 0$

   $\dfrac{dy}{dx} = 8x + 3$

   N.B. The derivative of a constant term, e.g., 6 is always zero.

(e) Equation: $y = \dfrac{1}{x} = x^{-1}$

$\dfrac{dy}{dx} = (-1 \times 1)x^{(-1-1)} = -x^{-2} = -\dfrac{1}{x^2}$

6. The distance s moved by a vehicle in time t is given by the equation $s = t^3 - 5t^2 + 3t$. Find (a) the initial velocity of the vehicle, (b) the velocity of the vehicle after 10 seconds, and (c) the acceleration of the vehicle after 10 seconds.
   Equation: $s = t^3 - 5t^2 + 3t$
   Velocity $= \dfrac{ds}{dt}$
   $\dfrac{ds}{dt} = 3t^2 - 10t + 3$

   (a) To determine the initial velocity the time t will be zero.
   When $t = 0$, $\dfrac{ds}{dt} =$
   $3 \times (0)^2 - (10 \times 0) + 3 = 0 - 0 + 3$
   $= 3$

   (b) To determine the velocity after 10 seconds $t = 10$.
   When $t = 10$,
   $\dfrac{ds}{dt} = 3 \times (10)^2 - (10 \times 10) + 3 =$
   $300 - 100 + 3 = 203$

   (c) Acceleration $= \dfrac{dv}{dt} = \dfrac{d^2s}{dt^2}$
   $\dfrac{d^2s}{dt^2} = 6t - 10$
   When $t = 10$,
   $\dfrac{d^2s}{dt^2} = (6 \times 10) - 10 = 60 - 10 = 50$

   The initial velocity of the vehcicle is 3 m/s with a velocity after 10 seconds of 203 m/s having an acceleration of 50 m/s^2.

7. The cross-section of a water trough is an isosceles triangle shown in Fig. 7.3. The length of the trough is 4 metres. Water enters at the rate of 1 cubic metre per minute. At what rate is the depth increasing at the end of 3 minutes.

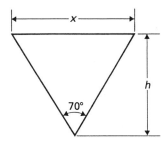

Figure 7.3

$\tan 35° = \dfrac{0.5x}{h}$, therefore $x = \dfrac{h \tan 35°}{0.5}$

$= 2h \tan 35° = 1.4h$

Volume of trough $V = csa \times$ length $=$
$0.5xh \times 4 = 2xh = 2.8h^2$

From $V = 2.8h^2, \dfrac{dV}{dh} = 5.6h$

For the trough: $\dfrac{dV}{dt} = \dfrac{dV}{dh} \times \dfrac{dh}{dt}$

Therefore $\dfrac{dV}{dt} = 5.6h \times \dfrac{dh}{dt}$

In 3 minutes water rate $= 1 \times 3 = 3 \text{ m}^3$

From $V = 2.8h^2$, $h = \sqrt{\dfrac{V}{2.8}} =$

$\sqrt{\dfrac{3}{2.8}} = 1.035 \text{ m}$

By substitution: $\dfrac{dV}{dt} = 5.6h \times \dfrac{dh}{dt}$

$\dfrac{dV}{dt} = 5.6 \times 1.035 \times \dfrac{dh}{dt}$

$\dfrac{dV}{dt} = 5.796 \dfrac{dh}{dt}$

Water entering at a rate of 1 m³/min
means that $\dfrac{dV}{dt} = 1$

By substitution: $\dfrac{dV}{dt} = 5.796 \dfrac{dh}{dt}$

$1 = 5.796 \cdot \dfrac{dh}{dt}$

$\dfrac{dh}{dt} = \dfrac{1}{5.796} = 0.1725$

The depth is increasing at a rate of 0.1725 metres per minute.

7.6 Exercises

Differentiate the following:

1. $y = 4x + 6$
2. $y = 3x - 7$
3. $y = 4 - 8x$
4. $y = 3 - 2x$
5. $y = \dfrac{4}{x}$
6. $y = \dfrac{6}{x}$
7. $y = 4 + \dfrac{2}{x}$
8. $y = 5 - \dfrac{3}{x}$
9. $y = 3x^2$
10. $y = 4x^3$
11. $y = 2x^4$
12. $y = 3x^5$
13. $y = x^2 + 10$
14. $y = x^3 + 4$
15. $y = 2x^2 + 5$
16. $y = 3x^2 + 2x$
17. $y = 2x^4 + 3x$
18. $y = 4x^5 - 5x$
19. $y = 3x^2 - 6x$
20. $y = 4x^3 - 3x$
21. $y = 2x^4 + 5x$
22. $R = aP^2$; find $\dfrac{dR}{dP}$
23. $s = \frac{1}{2}at^2$; find $\dfrac{ds}{dt}$
24. $V = 5L^3$; find $\dfrac{dV}{dL}$
25. $S = 10 + \dfrac{4t^3}{3}$; find $\dfrac{dS}{dt}$
26. $y = \dfrac{3}{x^2}$
27. $y = \sqrt{x}$
28. $y = 3x^2 + 4x$
29. $y = 3x^4 + 4x^3 + 5x^2$
30. $y = -6 + 4x - \dfrac{3x^2}{2} - 6x^3$

31. $y = (x - 3)^2$

32. $y = (x + 2)^3$

33. $y = \sqrt{x} + \dfrac{1}{\sqrt{x}}$

34. $y = \dfrac{3}{x^4}$

35. The distance s metres moved by a point in t seconds is given by $s = t^3 + 4t^2 + 2t$. Determine the velocity and acceleration after 4 seconds.

36. The distance moved by a vehicle along a line in t seconds is given in metres by $s = 2t^2 + 6t$. Find (a) the initial velocity of the vehicle, (b) the velocity of the vehicle after 3 seconds, and (c) the average velocity of the vehicle for the first 3 seconds.

37. A body moves so that its distance s metres at a time t seconds is given by the formula $s = 100t - 20t^2$.
    (a) Show that the acceleration is constant and find its magnitude.
    (b) Find the velocity at the end of 2 seconds.
    (CGLI)

38. Differentiate by inspection:
    (a) $y = 3x^4 + 3x + 2$;
    (b) $s = 8t^3 - 4t^2 + 2t + 3$.
    (WMAC)

39. A body moves s metres in t seconds where $s = 6 + 4t + 10t^2 - t^3$. By means of the calculus, find (a) its velocity at the end of 2 seconds, (b) its acceleration at the end of 3 seconds, (c) the value of t when the velocity is zero, and (d) the value of t when the acceleration is zero.
    (WMAC)

40. The displacement s metres of a certain body from a fixed point at time t seconds is given by $s = 3t^2 - 4t + 1$. Find (a) the value of s when $t = 3$ seconds, (b) the velocity of the body when $t = 0.1$ seconds, and (c) the time at which the velocity of the body is zero.
    (NWRAC)

41. The angular displacement θ radians of the armature of an electric motor after a time t seconds is given by the expression $\theta = 20t - 2t^2$. The angular velocity of the armature is the rate of change of angular displacement with time.
    (a) Determine the average angular velocity between $t = 1.5$ s and $t = 1.7$ s. (b) Write down an expression for the angular velocity at any instant. (c) Determine the time at which the angular velocity is zero and the corresponding value of the displacement. (d) Calculate the angular velocity at the instant $t = 3.4$ s giving the answer in rad/s and r/min.
    (WMAC)

42. Due to heat losses the useful heat received by a cylinder full of water from an immersion heater, taking a current of I amperes, is given by $W = 25I^2 - 6$. Calculate the value of $\dfrac{dW}{dI}$ and hence state the increase in W per ampere rise in current when $I = 5$ amperes.
    (EMFEC)

43. The angle θ radians turned through by a flywheel in t seconds is given by $\theta = 18 + 15t - 9t^2 + t^3$. If the angular velocity w and the angular acceleration α are given by $\dfrac{d\theta}{dt}$ and $\dfrac{dw}{dt}$ respectively, express w and α in terms of t. Hence find the values of w and α when t is 2. For what values of t is w zero?
    (NWRAC)

44. (a) If $y = 3x^2$, find the value of $\dfrac{dy}{dx}$

(b) Find $\dfrac{dy}{dx}$ if $y = (3x - 1)(x - 4)$.

(c) The equation of a curve is $y = ax^2 + bx + 2$, where a and b are constants.

When $x = 1$, $y = 4$, and $\dfrac{dy}{dx} = -2$,

find the values of a and b.

(NWRAC)

45. Find, by rule, the differential coefficients, with respect to x, of the following expressions:

(a) $x^2(2x + 1)$; (b) $\dfrac{(x + 1)^2}{x}$;

(c) $x^5(2x - 1)(x + 2)$.

(EMFEC)

46. Differentiate by rule

(a) $y = 4x^3 - 7x + 2$; (b) $y = x^2 + \dfrac{1}{x^2}$.

(EMFEC)

47. Differentiate with respect to x:

$$3x^{\frac{2}{3}} + x^{-\frac{1}{2}} + 5x^{1.2} + 4$$

(NWRAC)

48. A flywheel rotates according to the law $\theta = 28t - 3t^2$, θ being the angular rotation in radians taking place in t seconds. Find expressions for the angular velocity $\dfrac{d\theta}{dt}$ and the angular acceleration $\dfrac{d^2\theta}{dt^2}$. What is the value of t when $\dfrac{d\theta}{dt} = 0$? Find the value of θ for this value of t.

(NWRAC)

49. The relationship between the displacement, x metres, and the time, t seconds, of a moving body is $x = 2t^3 - 9t^2 + 12t + 4$. Find (a) the value of t when it comes to rest, (b) the value of t when its acceleration is zero, and (d) the acceleration when the velocity is zero.

(NCFE)

7.7 Turning points

A graph drawn from the equation $y = x^3 - 3x - 1$ gives a shape as shown in Fig. 7.4.

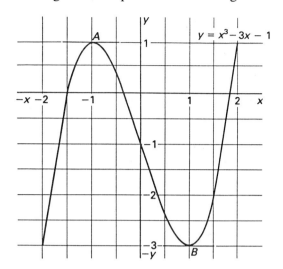

Figure 7.4

Points A and B are called turning points with point A being a maximum point and point B being a minimum point. Tangents draw at points A and B are parallel to the x axis giving a zero gradient, i.e., $\dfrac{dy}{dx} = 0$.

To determine the co-ordinates of the turning points we differentiate the equation twice, i.e., $\dfrac{d^2y}{dx^2}$ If $\dfrac{d^2y}{dx^2}$ is positive for a value of x we have found a minimum value for y.

If $\dfrac{d^2y}{dx^2}$ is negative for a

value of x we have found a maximum value for y.

i.e., $d\left(\dfrac{\frac{dy}{dx}}{dx}\right) = \dfrac{d}{dx}\left(\dfrac{dy}{dx}\right) = \dfrac{d^2(y)}{(dx)^2}$

Examples

8. Find the maximum and minimum value of the equation $y = x^3 - 3x - 1$.

Equation: $y = x^3 - 3x - 1$

$$\frac{dy}{dx} = 3x^{(3-1)} - 3x^{(1-1)}$$

$$\frac{dy}{dx} = 3x^2 - 3$$

Zero gradient $\frac{dy}{dx} = 0$ so $3x^2 - 3 = 0$

$$3x^2 = 3$$
$$x^2 = 1$$
$$x = \pm 1$$

For maximum and minimum values:

$$\frac{dy}{dx} = 3x^2 - 3$$

$$\frac{d^2y}{dx^2} = 6x$$

When $x = +1$

$$\frac{d^2y}{dx^2} = 6 \times 1 = 6$$

(Minimum turning point)

When $x = -1$

$$\frac{d^2y}{dx^2} = 6 \times -1 = -6$$

(Maximum turning point)

At the minimum turning point $x = +1$
Therefore $y = x^3 - 3x - 1 = 1^3 - (3 \times 1)$
$-1 = 1 - 3 - 1 = -3$
At the maximum turning point $x = -1$
Therefore $y = x^3 - 3x - 1 = (-1)^3 -$
$(3 \times -1) - 1 = -1 + 3 - 1 = (-1)^3 -$
At the turning points:
(A) Maximum $y = +1$
(B) Minimum $y = -3$

9. Determine the maximum rectangular area of a workshop that can be enclosed by sides of overall length 150 metres.
Let a = length of workshop
b = width of workshop
Perimeter $= a + b + a + b = 2(a + b)$
Therefore $2(a + b) = 150$
$a + b = 75$
Area of workshop $= A = ab$
From $a + b = 75$, $a = 75 - b$
$A = ab$

$$A = b(75 - b)$$
$$A = 75b - b^2$$

By differentiation:

$$\frac{dA}{db} = 75 - 2b$$

and $\frac{d^2A}{db^2} = -2$ (Giving a maximum case)

For maximum values: $\frac{dA}{db} = 0$

so $75 - 2b = 0$, $75 = 2b$, $b = 37.5$
Substitute $b = 37.5$ into $a = 75 - b$,
we get $a = 75 - 37.5 = 37.5$
The maximum rectangular area that can be enclosed by sides 150 metres in length are each 37.5 metres long, i.e., the workshop is square.

7.8 Exercises

Find the maximum and minimum values of the following equations:
1. $y = 2x^2 - 3x$
2. $y = 3x^2 - 4x + 1$
3. $y = x^3 - 4x$
4. $y = 2x^3 - 2x$
5. $y = x^3 - 4x - 2$
6. $y = \dfrac{1}{x} + x$
7. $y = 1 - 3x - x^2$
8. $y = 10x - x^3$
9. $y = 3x - x^3$
10. Find the maximum and minimum values of the expression $x^2 (2x + 1)$ and distinguish between them.

(EMFEC)

11. The volume of a cylindrical water tank, closed at each end, is 6750 cubic metres. Show that the total surface area S square metres is given by $S = 2\pi \left(r^2 + \dfrac{6750}{r} \right)$ where r is the radius in metres. Find the dimensions of the tank so that its total surface area is a minimum.

(WJEC)

12. If $y = x^2 + \dfrac{16}{x}$, derive an expression for $\dfrac{dy}{dx}$. Sketch the graph of the original function, clearly indicating on the graph where $\dfrac{dy}{dx} = 0$.

(CGLI)

13. Draw the graph of $y = 2x^3 - 3x^2 - 9x + 9$ for values of x from $x = -2$ to $x = 3$ and hence determine within this range (a) the maximum and minimum values of y, and the values of x at which these occur, (b) the three solutions of the equation.

(YHCFE)

14. Plot the graph of $y = x^3 - 4x$ for values of x between -3 and $+3$, and indicate the maximum and minimum values of the expression on the graph. Add to the graph a suitable straight line and hence solve the equation $x^3 - 3x - 1 = 0$.

(WMAC)

15. An open metal box is x metres wide, $3x$ metres long, and has a volume of 21 cubic metres. Show that (a) the height of the box is given by $h = \dfrac{7}{x^2}$ metres, (b) the surface area of metal used in the construction is $3x^2 + \dfrac{56}{x}$.

(EMFEC)

16. Using the information from Exercise 15, plot a graph of area against x from $x = 1$ to $x = 5$ and hence determine the dimensions of the box for minimum surface area, and the value of the minimum surface area.

(EMFEC)

17. A two-stage compressor has an interstage pressure of x. The work done W by the compressor is

$$W = 10\left[\frac{x^2}{225} + 18225x^{-2} - 2\right].$$

Show that the work done is a minimum when $x = 45$.

(NWRAC)

18. A sheet metal box, rectangular, without a lid, has square ends of side x metres. If the volume is $20\frac{5}{6}$ m^3, show that the area of sheet metal is given by $A = 2x^2 + \dfrac{125}{2x}$. Find the least area of sheet metal to construct the box. Overlapping of metal may be ignored.

(WJEC)

7.9 Graphical derivation of the differentiation of $\sin x$ and $\cos x$

A graph of $\sin x$ is shown in Fig. 7.5

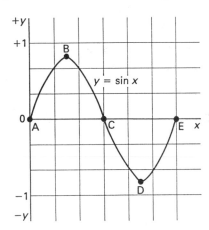

Figure 7.5

By observation:
At point B the gradient is parallel to the x axis, therefore $\dfrac{dy}{dx} = 0$.

At point D the gradient is parallel to the x axis, therefore $\dfrac{dy}{dx} = 0$.

At point A the gadient has a positive value thus making point A' a maximum positive value.

At point C the gradient has a negative value thus making point C' a minimum negative value.

At point E the gradient has a positive value thus making point E' a maximum positive value.

From this information a graph of $\frac{dy}{dx}$ can be drawn as shown in Fig. 7.6.

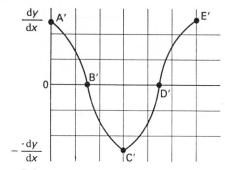

Figure 7.6

By observation this graph is recognized as the shape of cos x. Therefore when $y = \sin x$, $\frac{dy}{dx} = \cos x$.

A similar exercise can be carried out to show that when $y = \cos x, \frac{dy}{dx} = -\sin x$.

Examples

10. Differentiate the following: (a) sin x, (b) cos x, (c) 2 sin x, (d) 3 cos x, (e) sin 3x, (f) cos 4x, (g) 2 sin 4x, (h) 3 cos 2x, (i) 3 sin x + 4 cos x, (j) 4 cos 2x + 3 sin 5x, (k) 2 cos 3x − sin x.

Answers:

(a) When $y = \sin x, \frac{dy}{dx} = \cos x$

(b) When $y = \cos x, \frac{dy}{dx} = -\sin x$

(c) When $y = 2 \sin x, \frac{dy}{dx} = 2 \cos x$

(d) When $y = 3 \cos x, \frac{dy}{dx} = -3 \sin x$

(e) When $y = \sin 3x, \frac{dy}{dx} = 3 \cos 3x$

(f) When $y = \cos 4x, \frac{dy}{dx} = -4 \sin 4x$

(g) When $y = 2 \sin 4x, \frac{dy}{dx} = (4 \times 2) \cos 4x = 8 \cos 4x$

(h) When $y = 3 \cos 2x, \frac{dy}{dx} = -(2 \times 3) \sin 2x = -6 \sin 2x$

(i) When $y = 3 \sin x + 4 \cos x$, $\frac{dy}{dx} = 3 \cos x - 4 \sin x$

(j) When $y = 4 \cos 2x + 3 \sin 5x$
$\frac{dy}{dx} = -(2 \times 4) \sin 2x + (5 \times 3) \cos 5x$
$\frac{dy}{dx} = -8 \sin 2x + 15 \cos 5x$

(k) When $y = 2 \cos 3x - \sin x$
$\frac{dy}{dx} = -(3 \times 2) \sin 3x - \cos x$
$\frac{dy}{dx} = -6 \sin 3x - \cos x$

11. An alternating voltage is given by the expression $v = 20 \sin 50t$ where v is in volts and t in seconds. Calculate the rate of change of voltage when $t = 0.02$ seconds.

Equation: $v = 20 \sin 50t$

Rate of change of voltage $= \frac{dv}{dt}$

From $v = 20 \sin 50t$,
$\frac{dv}{dt} = (50 \times 20) \cos 50t = 1000 \cos 50t$

When $t = 0.02$ seconds,
$\frac{dv}{dt} = 1000 \cos (50 \times 0.02)$

$\frac{dv}{dt} = 1000 \cos 1$
(remember that 1 is in radians)

$$\frac{dv}{dt} = 1000 \times 0.5403$$

$$\frac{dv}{dt} = 540.3$$

The rate of change of voltage is 540.3 V/s.

7.10 Exercises

Differentiate the following:

1. sin x
2. cos x
3. 2 sin x
4. 3 cos x
5. 4 sin x
6. 5 cos x
7. sin $2x$
8. cos $3x$
9. 2 sin $3x$
10. 3 sin $4x$
11. 2 cos $3x$
12. 4 cos $2x$
13. sin x + cos x
14. 2 sin x + cos x
15. sin x + 3 cos x
16. sin $4x$ + cos x
17. sin x + cos $3x$
18. sin $3x$ + cos $2x$
19. sin $4x$ + cos $3x$
20. 2 sin $3x$ + 3 cos $4x$
21. 3 sin $4x$ + 5 cos $6x$
22. 4 cos $2x$ + 2 sin $3x$
23. 3 sin x − 2 cos x
24. 3 sin $2x$ − 4 cos $3x$
25. 2 sin $4x$ − 3 cos $5x$
26. −3 sin x
27. −4 cos x
28. −2 sin $3x$
29. −4 cos $2x$
30. −3 sin x + 4 cos x
31. −4 sin $2x$ + 3 cos $5x$
32. −2 cos $4x$ − 3 sin $5x$
33. x^2 + sin x
34. cos x + $3x^2$
35. cos $2x$ + $6x^3$
36. 3 sin $2x$ + 4 cos $5x$ + $3x^2$ + $5x$

37. An alternating current is given by $i = 40$ sin $150t$ where t is the time in seconds. Calculate the rate of change of current when $t = 0.01$ seconds.

38. An alternating voltage is given by $v = 150$ sin $100t$ where t is the time in seconds. Calculate the rate of change of voltage when $t = 0.0156$ seconds.

39. The instantaneous value of a certain voltage waveform at time t seconds is given by the expression $v = 200$ sin $100\pi t$. Sketch a graph of the waveform for values of t between 0 and 0.01 s using intervals of 0.00125 s. Determine the rate of change of v at the instants when $t = 0.005$ s and $t = 0.0075$ s.

(NWRAC)

40. Plot a graph of $y = 5$ sin $2x$ from $x = 0$ to $x = \pi$. Use the graph to verify that $\frac{dy}{dx} = 10$ cos $2x$, for values of x equal to $\frac{\pi}{6}$ and $\frac{2\pi}{3}$.

41. Plot a graph of $y = 4$ cos $2x$ from $x = 0$ to $x = \pi$. Use the graph to verify that $\frac{dy}{dx} = -8$ sin $2x$ for the value $x = \frac{\pi}{6}$ and $\frac{2\pi}{3}$.

42. Plot a graph of $y = \cos x$ for values of x from $x = 0°$ to $x = 360°$. Measure the gradients at a number of points and then plot a graph for $\frac{dy}{dx}$. Derive from the graph that when $y = \cos x, \frac{dy}{dx} = -\sin x$.

130

Answers

Exercises 7.2

1. 12
2. −12
3. 5
4. 5
5. 17
6. 24
7. −18
8. −10
9. −9
   15
10. 28
11. −6
    6
12. 9
    21
13. −10
    14
14. −8
    10
15. 12
    12
16. 144
17. 14
    14
18. 58
    100
19. 155
    155
20. 187

Exercises 7.4

1. $4x$
2. $6x^2$
3. $2x$
4. $3x^2$
5. $2x + 2$
6. $3x^2 + 3$
7. $2x + 3$
8. $3x^2 + 2$
9. $2x - 2$
10. $3x^2 + 1$

11. 3
12. $8t - 3$
13. $2\pi r$
14. $-\dfrac{1}{x^2}$
15. $4x$
16. $2x - 3$

Exercises 7.6

1. 4
2. 3
3. −8
4. −2
5. $-\dfrac{4}{x^2}$
6. $-\dfrac{6}{x^2}$
7. $-\dfrac{2}{x^2}$
8. $\dfrac{3}{x^2}$
9. $6x$
10. $12x^2$
11. $8x^3$
12. $15x^4$
13. $2x$
14. $3x^2$
15. $4x$
16. $6x + 2$
17. $8x^3 + 3$
18. $20x^4 - 5$
19. $6x - 6$
20. $12x^2 - 3$
21. $8x^3 + 5$
22. $2aP$
23. at
24. $15L^2$
25. $4t^2$
26. $-\dfrac{6}{x^3}$
27. $0.5\, x^{-0.5}$
28. $6x + 4$
29. $12x^3 + 12x^2 + 10x$
30. $4 - 3x - 18x^2$

31. $2x - 6$
32. $3x^2 + 12x + 12$
33. $\dfrac{0.5}{x^{0.5}} - \dfrac{0.5}{x^{1.5}}$
34. $-\dfrac{12}{x^5}$
35. 82 m/s
    32 m/s^2
36. 6 m/s
    18 m/s
    12 m/s
37. -40 m/s^2
    20 m/s
38. $12x^3 + 3$
    $24t^2 - 8t + 2$
39. 32 m/s
    2 m/s^2
    6.9 s
    3.3 s
40. 16 m
    -3.4 m/s
    0.67 s
41. 13.6 rad/s
    $20 - 4t$
    5 s
    50 rad
    6.4 rad/s
    61.1 r/min
42. $50I$
    250
43. -9
    -6
    1 and 5
44. $6x$
    $6x - 13$
    -6
    10
45. $6x^2 + 2x$
    $1 - \dfrac{2}{x^2}$
    $2x^4(7x^2 + 9x - 5)$
46. $12x^2 - 7$
    $2x - \dfrac{2}{x^3}$

47. $\dfrac{2}{x^{1/3}} - \dfrac{0.5}{x^{1.5}} + 6x^{0.2}$
48. 4.67 s
    65.3 rad
49. $t = 1$ or 2
    1.5 s
    -1.5 m/s
    ± 6 m/s^2

Exercises 7.8

1. -1.125 min
2. -0.33 min
3. -3.08 min
   $+3.08$ max
4. -0.59 min
5. $+0.77$ min
   -0.77 max
6. $+2$ min
   -2 max
7. $+3.25$ max
8. -12.17 min
   $+12.17$ max
9. -2 min
   $+2$ max
10. 0 min
    $+0.037$ max
11. $r = 15$ m
12. $2x - \dfrac{16}{x^2}$
13. $x = -0.6$
    14 max
    $x = 1.7$
    -6 min
    -1.95
    0.8
    2.4
14. -3 min
    $+3$ max
    1.5
    1.8
    -0.35
15. Proof
16. 2.1 m
    6.3 m

132

1.6 m

40 m^2

17. Proof

18. 37.5 m^2

Exercises 7.10

1. $\cos x$
2. $-\sin x$
3. $2 \cos x$
4. $-3 \sin x$
5. $4 \cos x$
6. $-5 \sin x$
7. $2 \cos 2x$
8. $-3 \sin 3x$
9. $6 \cos 3x$
10. $12 \cos 4x$
11. $-6 \sin 3x$
12. $-8 \sin 2x$
13. $\cos x - \sin x$
14. $2 \cos x - \sin x$
15. $\cos x - 3 \sin x$
16. $4 \cos 4x - \sin x$
17. $\cos x - 3 \sin 3x$
18. $3 \cos 3x - 2 \sin 2x$

19. $4 \cos 4x - 3 \sin 3x$
20. $6 \cos 3x - 12 \sin 4x$
21. $12 \cos 4x - 30 \sin 6x$
22. $-8 \sin 2x + 6 \cos 3x$
23. $3 \cos x + 2 \sin x$
24. $6 \cos 2x + 12 \sin 3x$
25. $8 \cos 4x + 15 \sin 5x$
26. $-3 \cos x$
27. $4 \sin x$
28. $-6 \cos 3x$
29. $8 \sin 2x$
30. $-3 \cos x - 4 \sin x$
31. $-8 \cos 2x - 15 \sin 5x$
32. $8 \sin 4x - 15 \cos 5x$
33. $2x + \cos x$
34. $6x - \sin x$
35. $18x^2 - 2 \sin 2x$
36. $6 \cos 2x - 20 \sin 5x + 6x + 5$
37. 423.8 A
38. 160 V
39. -7.27 V/s

    44437 V/s
40. Proof
41. Proof
42. Proof

8 Integral Calculus

8.1 Indefinite integrals

In Section 7.5 we found that when $y = 4x^3$ that $\frac{dy}{dx} = 12x^2$. If we reverse the process and start with $\frac{dy}{dx} = 12x^2$ then $y = 4x^3$. This reverse process is called integration and given the symbol $\int$. Therefore $y = \int 12x^2 \, dx = 4x^3$. There is a flaw in this argument; the original equation might have been $y = 4x^3 + 5$, and when differentiated the 5 would have disappeared. To cater for this situation we introduce the constant of integration C.

Examples

1. Given $\frac{dy}{dx} = 3x^4 + 2x^3$, find an equation for y.

   By differentiation: $\frac{dy}{dx} = 3x^4 + 2x^3$

   Consider each term separately:

   Term $3x^4$: By observation, to have obtained x^4 we need a term x^5. By differentiation when $y = x^5$ we get $\frac{dy}{dx} = 5x^4$. In order to get $3x^4$ we need $\frac{3x^5}{5}$.

   Check: $y = \frac{3x^5}{5}$

   $\frac{dy}{dx} = \frac{5 \times 3x^4}{5} = 3x^4$.

   Term $2x^3$: By observation, to have obtained x^3 we need a term x^4. By differentiation when $y = x^4$

we get $\frac{dy}{dx} = 4x^3$. In order to get $2x^3$ we need $\frac{2x^4}{4}$.

Check: $y = \frac{2x^4}{4}$

$\frac{dy}{dx} = \frac{4 \times 2x^3}{4} = 2x^3$.

Final solution:

Given $\frac{dy}{dx} = 3x^4 + 2x^3$ then

$$y = \frac{3x^5}{5} + \frac{2x^4}{4} + C$$

Integrals in which C is not determined are called indefinite integrals.

In general: $\int x^n \, dx = \frac{x^{n+1}}{n+1} + C.$

Note: The left-hand expression is read aloud as 'The (indefinite) integral of x to the n with respect to x'. The term dx indicates the variable that is the subject of the integration process.

2. Integrate $x^3 + 3x^2 + x$ with respect to x.

   $\int x^3 + 3x^2 + x. \, dx = \frac{x^4}{4} + \frac{3x^3}{3} + \frac{x^2}{2} + C$

   $\qquad = \frac{x^4}{4} + x^3 + \frac{x^2}{2} + C$

3. Integrate $x^{1.4} + \frac{1}{x^3}$ with respect to x.

   $\int x^{1.4} + \frac{1}{x^3} \, dx = \int x^{1.4} + x^{-3} \, dx$

   $\qquad = \frac{x^{2.4}}{2.4} + \frac{x^{-2}}{-2} + C$

   $\qquad = \frac{x^{2.4}}{2.4} - \frac{1}{2x^2} + C$

8.2 Exercises

Integrate the following with respect to x:

1. $x^3 + 4x$
2. $x^{3.5}$
3. $x^{3.2} + x^2$
4. $\dfrac{1}{x^2}$
5. $\dfrac{1}{x^3}$
6. $\dfrac{1}{x^4}$
7. $\dfrac{1}{x^5}$
8. $x^3 + \dfrac{1}{x^3}$
9. $2x^3 + x$
10. $3x^2 + x$
11. $3x^3 + x^2$
12. $4x^3 + 3x^2$
13. $3x^4 + 2x^3 + 4x$
14. $5x^3 + 3x^2 + 2x$
15. $6x^4 + \sqrt{x}$
16. $3x^3 + \sqrt{x}$
17. $x^6 + 4x^5 + 3x^3 + \sqrt{x}$
18. $3x^4 + \dfrac{1}{x^2} + \sqrt{x}$
19. $8 - \sqrt{x}$
20. $x^{1.2} + \dfrac{1}{x^4} - 4\sqrt{x}$

8.3 Definite integrals

An indefinite integral does not reveal a calculated value but with a definite integral it is possible to have a numerical value.

Examples

4. Calculate a value for the definite integral
$$\int_{2}^{4} 6x \, dx.$$

$$\int_{2}^{4} 6x \, dx = \left[\frac{6x^2}{2} + C \right]_{2}^{4} = \left[3x^2 + C \right]_{2}^{4}$$

The numerical values of 2 and 4 mean that $x = 2$ and $x = 4$.

When $x = 4$, integral $= 3x^2 + C = 48 + C$
When $x = 2$, integral $= 3x^2 + C = 12 + C$

$$\int_{2}^{4} 6x \, dx = (48 + C) - (12 + C)$$
$$= 48 + C - 12 - C = 36$$

$$\int_{2}^{4} 6x \, dx = 36$$

The constant C disappeared in this calculation and will disappear in all calculations when an upper and lower limit are given. For definite integrals the constant C is therefore omitted.

5. Integrate the following: $\displaystyle\int_{0}^{2} 3x^2 + x \, dx.$

$$\int_{0}^{2} 3x^2 + x \, dx = \left[\frac{3x^3}{3} + \frac{x^2}{2} \right]_{0}^{2}$$

$$= \left[x^3 + 0.5\,x^2 \right]_{0}^{2}$$

$$= (8 + 2) - (0 + 0) = 10$$
$$\int_{0}^{2} 3x^2 + x \, dx = 10$$

8.4 Exercises

Work out the following definite integrals:

1. $\displaystyle\int_{0}^{2} 4x \, dx.$

2. $\displaystyle\int_{0}^{3} 2x^2 \, dx.$

3. $\displaystyle\int_{0}^{3} 3x^3 \, dx.$

4. $\displaystyle\int_{0}^{2} x^4 \, dx.$

5. $\displaystyle\int_1^2 3x + 2\,dx.$

6. $\displaystyle\int_1^3 3x^2 + x\,dx$

7. $\displaystyle\int_1^4 2x^3 + x^2\,dx.$

8. $\displaystyle\int_1^3 x + x^2 + x^3\,dx.$

9. $\displaystyle\int_2^4 2x + x^3\,dx.$

10. $\displaystyle\int_2^3 \frac{1}{x^2}\,dx.$

11. $\displaystyle\int_2^6 x^2 - 4x\,dx.$

12. $\displaystyle\int_2^4 1 - x\,dx.$

13. $\displaystyle\int_2^3 \sqrt{x}\,dx.$

14. $\displaystyle\int_0^4 3x^2 - 2x + 4\,dx.$

15. $\displaystyle\int_1^3 5 - x^2\,dx.$

16. $\displaystyle\int_1^5 \sqrt{x} + x^2\,dx.$

17. $\displaystyle\int_{-3}^0 5 - x^4\,dx.$

18. $\displaystyle\int_{-2}^0 3 - x^2\,dx.$

19. $\displaystyle\int_{-2}^3 2x^{-3} + x^3\,dx.$

20. Evaluate:

(a) $\displaystyle\int_2^3 3\,dx.$

(b) $\displaystyle\int_0^2 6x^2 - 12x + 5\,dx.$

(EMFEC)

21. Evaluate the following:

(a) $\displaystyle\int_0^1 6x^2 - 2x\,dx.$

(b) $\displaystyle\int_0^1 12x^3 + 6x^2 - 5x + 1\,dx.$

(EMFEC)

22. Evaluate:

$\displaystyle\int_0^2 3x^2 + 2\,dx.$

$\displaystyle\int_{-2}^3 8x^3 - 3x^2\,dx.$

(EMFEC)

23. Evaluate:

$\displaystyle\int_{-1}^0 4x\,dx.$

$\displaystyle\int_2^5 3x^2 - x + 4\,dx.$

(EMFEC)

24. Evaluate:

$\displaystyle\int_{-1}^2 8x - 3\,dx.$

25. Evaluate

$\displaystyle\int_1^3 \frac{x^3 + 3}{x^2}\,dx.$

26. Evaluate:

(a) $\displaystyle\int y^2\,dx,$ when $y = 1 - x.$

(b) $\displaystyle\int_1^2 2x^4\,dx$

(WMAC)

27. The gradient of a curve is given by the expression $\dfrac{dy}{dx} = 3x - 3$ and is known to pass through the point (1,2). Find the equation of the curve.

(WMAC)

8.5 Area under a curve

The interpretation of a definite integral is that it represents the area between the function $f(x)$ and the x axis between the limits given. Care must be taken to work out areas above the x axis separately from those below the x axis, in order to take into account positive and negative values of x.

Example

6. Find the area between the curve $y = x$ and the x axis between the values $x = 0$ and $x = 10$.

   Equation: $y = x$

   $$\text{Area under curve} = \int_0^{10} x \, dx = \left[\frac{x^2}{2} \right]_0^{10}$$

   $$= \frac{10^2}{2} - 0 = 50 \text{ units}^2$$

   A check on $y = x$ can be made by plotting the curve as shown in Fig. 8.1

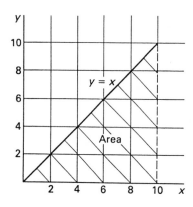

Figure 8.1

$$\text{Area of triangle} = \tfrac{1}{2} \text{ base} \times \text{perpendicular height}$$
$$= \tfrac{1}{2} \times 10 \times 10$$
$$= 50 \text{ units}^2$$

8.6 Exercises

Find the area between the curves for the given equation, the x axis and the ordinates for the following (1–6):

1. $y = x^2 - 3x + 4$, $x = 2$ and $x = 4$.

2. $y = 8x - 4x^2$, $x = 2$ and $x = 5$.

3. $y = 2 - 3x - x^2$, $x = 2$ and $x = 6$.

4. $y = x^2 - 5x + 6$, $x = 2$ and $x = 3$.

5. $y = 8x - x^2$, $x = 0$ and $x = 8$.

6. $y = x^3$, $x = 0$ and $x = 4$.

7. Sketch the graphs of $y = x^2$ and $y = 5x - 4$. Calculate the co-ordinates of their points of intersection and the area of the segment of the curve cut off by the line.
   (WJEC)

8. Sketch the curve $y = \dfrac{1}{(x - 2)}$ between the limits $x = -2$ and $x = 6$. Find the area bounded by the ordinates as $x = 3$ and $x = 6$, the curve and the x axis.
   (WMAC)

9. Sketch the curve $y = \tfrac{2}{3}\sqrt{36 - x^2}$ taking values of x at unit intervals from $x = 0$ to $x = 6$. Determine the area bounded by the curve and the x and y axes.
   (NCFE)

10. Variables x and y are connected by the relationship $y = \sqrt{10x - x^2}$. Sketch a graph of y against x for the whole range over which the quantity under the root sign is positive. Find the area enclosed between the graph and the x axis.
    (NCFE)

11. Find the area bounded by the curve $y = x^3 - 4x$, the x-axis, and ordinates $x = 0$, $x = 2$.
    (CGLI)

12. If $y = 2x^3 - 3x^2 - 36x - 1$, find the area between the curve, the x axis, and the ordinates at $x = 1$ and $x = 3$.

(WJEC)

13. Find the area enclosed between the curve $y = 3x^2 + 5$, the x axis, the ordinates at $x = 1$ and $x = 3$.

(WJEC)

8.7 Integrals of $\sin x$ and $\cos x$

Because integration is the reverse process of differentiation:

(a) $\displaystyle\int \sin x \, dx = -\cos x + C$

(b) $\displaystyle\int \cos x \, dx = \sin x + C$

Examples

7. Integrate the following with respect to x:
   (a) $\sin 2x$; (b) $\cos 3x$; (c) $\cos (2x + \theta)$.

$$\int \sin 2x \, dx = -\frac{\cos 2x}{2} + C$$

$$\int \cos 3x \, dx = \frac{\sin 3x}{3} + C$$

$$\int \cos (2x + \theta) \, dx = \frac{\sin (2x + \theta)}{2} + C$$

8. Evaluate the integral:

$$\int_0^{\pi/2} (\sin 2x - \cos 2x) \, dx$$

$$= \left[-\frac{\cos 2x}{2} - \frac{\sin 2x}{2} \right]_0^{\pi/2}$$

$$= \left(-\frac{\cos \pi}{2} - \frac{\sin \pi}{2} \right)$$

$$\quad - \left(-\frac{\cos 0}{2} - \frac{\sin 0}{2} \right)$$

$$= (\tfrac{1}{2} - 0) - (-\tfrac{1}{2} - 0)$$

$$= \tfrac{1}{2} + \tfrac{1}{2}$$

$$= 1$$

$$\int_0^{\pi/2} (\sin 2x - \cos 2x) \, dx = 1$$

8.8 Exercises

Evaluate the following integrals all between the limits of 0 and $\dfrac{\pi}{2}$

1. $\sin x$.
2. $\cos x$.
3. $\sin 2x$.
4. $\cos 2x$.
5. $2 \cos 4x$.
6. $\sin x + \cos x$.
7. $3 \sin 2x + \cos x$.
8. $3 \sin 4x + 2 \cos 3x$.
9. $2 \sin 4x - 3 \cos 2x$.
10. $\cos 3x - 4 \sin x$.
11. $x^2 + 3 \sin 4x$.
12. $x^3 + 4 \cos 2x$.
13. $3x^4 + \sin x + \cos x$.
14. $\cos 5x + 3x^5 - 2 \sin 3x$.
15. $\sin 3x + 4 \cos 6x + \sqrt{x}$

Answers

Exercises 8.2

1. $\frac{1}{4}x^4 + 2x^2$
2. $\dfrac{x^{4.5}}{4.5}$
3. $\dfrac{x^{4.2}}{4.2} + \dfrac{x^3}{3}$
4. $-\dfrac{1}{x}$
5. $-\dfrac{1}{2x^2}$
6. $-\dfrac{1}{3x^3}$
7. $-\dfrac{1}{4x^4}$
8. $\frac{1}{4}x^4 - \dfrac{1}{2x^2}$
9. $\frac{1}{2}x^4 + \frac{1}{2}x^2$
10. $x^3 + \frac{1}{2}x^2$
11. $\frac{3}{4}x^4 + \frac{1}{3}x^3$
12. $x^4 + x^3$
13. $0.6x^5 + 0.5x^4 + 0.5x^2$

14. $1.25x^4 + x^3 + x^2$
15. $1.2x^5 + \frac{2}{3}x^{3/2}$
16. $\frac{3}{4}x^4 + \frac{2}{3}x^{3/2}$
17. $\dfrac{x^7}{7} + \frac{2}{3}x^6 + \frac{3}{4}x^4 + \frac{2}{3}x^{3/2}$
18. $0.6x^5 - \dfrac{1}{x} + \frac{2}{3}x^{3/2}$
19. $8x - \frac{2}{3}x^{3/2}$
20. $\dfrac{x^{2.2}}{2.2} + \ - \dfrac{1}{3x^3} - 2\frac{2}{3}x^{3/2}$

Exercises 8.4

1. 8
2. 18
3. 60.75
4. 6.4
5. 6.5
6. 30
7. 148.5
8. 32.67
9. 72
10. 0.166
11. $5\frac{1}{3}$
12. -4
13. 1.579
14. 64
15. $1\frac{1}{3}$
16. 48.12
17. -33.6
18. $3\frac{1}{3}$
19. 16.39
20. 2
21. 1
    3.5
22. 12
    95
23. -2
    118.5

24. 3
25. 6
26. $x - x^2 + \frac{1}{3}x^3$
    12.4
27. $y = 1.5x^2 - 3x$

Exercises 8.6

1. 8.67
2. -72
3. $-109\frac{1}{3}$
4. -0.166
5. 85.33
6. 64
7. 4.5
8. 1.386
9. 18.8
10. 39.3
11. -4
12. -132
13. 36

Exercises 8.8

1. 1
2. 1
3. 1
4. 0
5. 0
6. 0
7. 3.5
8. $-\frac{2}{3}$
9. 0
10. -4.333
11. 1.292
12. 1.522
13. 7.738
14. 7.04
15. 0.98

9 Matrix Algebra

9.1 The matrix

A matrix is an arrangement of numbers or letters in rows and columns, e.g., a row $[2 \quad 4 \quad 6]$ or a column $\begin{bmatrix} 2 \\ 4 \\ 6 \end{bmatrix}$

A square matrix is $\begin{bmatrix} a & b \\ c & d \end{bmatrix}$ from which the determinant $D = ad - cb$. A singular matrix is one whose determinant is zero.

Example

1. By calculating its determinant, state whether the following matrix is singular:

$$A = \begin{bmatrix} 4 & -2 \\ -6 & 3 \end{bmatrix}$$
$$D_A = (4 \times 3) - (-6 \times -2)$$
$$= (12) - (12)$$
$$= 12 - 12$$
$$= 0$$

Since D_A equals zero the matrix A must be singular.

9.2 Solution of simultaneous equations

The following proof is fairly lengthy, but the end result will help to solve simultaneous equations more quickly.

$$a_1x + b_1y + c_1 = 0 \qquad \text{Eq. (1)}$$
$$a_2x + b_2y + c_2 = 0 \qquad \text{Eq. (2)}$$

To determine an equation for x:

Eq. (1) $\times b_2$ $\quad a_1b_2x + b_1b_2y + b_2c_1 = 0$
Eq. (2) $\times b_1$ $\quad a_2b_1x + b_1b_2y + b_1c_2 = 0$

Subtract:
$$(a_1b_2x - a_2b_1x) + (b_2c_1 - b_1c_2) = 0$$
$$x(a_1b_2 - a_2b_1) = b_1c_2 - b_2c_1$$
$$x = \frac{b_1c_2 - b_2c_1}{a_1b_2 - a_2b_1} \qquad \text{Eq. (3)}$$

To determine an equation for y:

Eq. (1) $\times a_2$ $\quad a_1a_2x + a_2b_1y + a_2c_1 = 0$
Eq. (2) $\times a_1$ $\quad a_1a_2x + a_1b_2y + a_1c_2 = 0$

Subtract
$$(a_2b_1y - a_1b_2y) + (a_2c_1 - a_1c_2) = 0$$
$$y(a_2b_1 - a_1b_2) = a_1c_2 - a_2c_1$$
$$y = \frac{a_1c_2 - a_2c_1}{a_2b_1 - a_1b_2}$$
$$-y = \frac{a_1c_2 - a_2c_1}{a_1b_2 - a_2b_1} \qquad \text{Eq. (4)}$$

From Eq. (3) $\quad a_1b_2 - a_2b_1 = \dfrac{b_1c_2 - b_2c_1}{x}$

From Eq. (4) $\quad a_1b_2 - a_2b_1 = \dfrac{a_1c_2 - a_2c_1}{-y}$

Therefore
$$\frac{x}{b_1c_2 - b_2c_1} = \frac{-y}{a_1c_2 - a_2c_1} = \frac{1}{a_1b_2 - a_2b_1}$$
$$\text{Eq. (5)}$$

The denominators of Eq. (5) can now be written in determinant form as follows:

$$\frac{x}{\begin{vmatrix} b_1 & c_1 \\ b_2 & c_2 \end{vmatrix}} = \frac{-y}{\begin{vmatrix} a_1 & c_1 \\ a_2 & c_2 \end{vmatrix}} = \frac{1}{\begin{vmatrix} a_1 & b_1 \\ a_2 & b_2 \end{vmatrix}}$$

Each determinant can now be calculated using the rule from Sec. 9.1.

Example

2. Solve the following simultaneous equation:
$$2x + 5y - 10 = 0$$
$$x + 2y - 3 = 0$$

The equation rewritten becomes

$$\frac{x}{D_1} = \frac{-y}{D_2} = \frac{1}{D}$$

From the simultaneous equation:

$$D_1 = \begin{vmatrix} 5 & -10 \\ 2 & -3 \end{vmatrix} = (5 \times -3) - (2 \times -10)$$
$$= -15 + 20 = 5$$

$$D_2 = \begin{vmatrix} 2 & -10 \\ 1 & -3 \end{vmatrix} = (2 \times -3) - (1 \times -10)$$
$$= 6 + 10 = 4$$

$$D = \begin{vmatrix} 2 & 5 \\ 1 & 2 \end{vmatrix} = (2 \times 2) - (1 \times 5)$$
$$= 4 - 5 = -1$$

From $\dfrac{x}{D_1} = \dfrac{-y}{D_2} = \dfrac{1}{D}$ we now have

$$\frac{x}{5} = \frac{-y}{4} = \frac{1}{-1}$$

Then $\dfrac{x}{5} = \dfrac{1}{-1}$ $x = -5$

Also $\dfrac{-y}{4} = \dfrac{1}{-1}$ $y = 4$

Check: Use Eq. (1)

$$2x + 5y - 10 = 0$$
$$(2 \times -5) + (5 \times 4) - 10 = 0$$
$$-10 + 20 - 10 = 0$$
$$-20 + 20 = 0$$
$$0 = 0$$

The solution of the simultaneous equation is that $x = -5$ and $y = 4$.

9.3 Exercises

By calculating the determinants of the following, state which are singular. (1–4)

1. | 8 | −4 |
   | −12 | 6. |

2. | 2 | 6 |
   | 5 | 8. |

3. | 6 | −7 |
   | 5 | 3. |

4. | 4 | −8 |
   | 3 | −6. |

Solve the following simultaneous equations:

5. $4x + 10y = 20$
   $2x + 4y = 6$

6. $3x + 7y = 27$
   $5x + 2y = 16$

7. $4a + 3b = 38$
   $3a - 1.5b = 21$

8. $4a - 2b = 18$
   $6a - 14y = 38$

9. $5x - 7y = 0$
   $7x + 5y = 74$

10. $8x - 12y = -5$
    $4x - 3y = -0.5$

11. Currents I_1 and I_2 in a simple network are related as follows:
    $$0.5I_1 + 0.6I_2 = 7$$
    $$1.2I_1 + 0.4I_2 = 9$$
    Solve the simultaneous equations to find I_1 and I_2.

    (CGLI)

Answers

Exercises 9.3

1. Singular
2. Not singular
3. Not singular
4. Singular
5. −5, 4
6. 2, 3
7. 8, 2
8. 4, −1
9. 7, 5
10. 0.375, 0.67
11. 5, 7.5